100 YEARS OF POPULAR

Volume 1

Malcolm Pike

20s

Series Editor:
Carol Cuellar

Editorial and Production:
Artemis Music Limited

Design and Production:
JPCreativeGroup.com

Published 2003

International Music Publications

International Music Publications Limited
Griffin House 161 Hammersmith Road London W6 8BS England

CONTENTS

20s

EGYPTIAN BLEND CIGARETTES
FEZ
MANUFACTURED IN LONDON
MANUFACTURED IN LONDON
B. MORRIS & SONS LTD
MANSELL ST
LONDON E.

"It was the best of times, it was the worst of times." Our apologies to the great Charles Dickens, but the opening sentence from his 1859 classic, *A Tale Of Two Cities*, captures the complex and often contradictory spirit of the 1920s. Yes, the Great War had been won and the Kaiser vanquished, but at a frightful cost in lives, property, and innocence. Technology raced ahead at a dizzying pace, amazing even the most world-weary observer. Air travel, a novelty before the war, was becoming almost common. And hadn't the world cheered when Alexander Fleming of St. Mary's Hospital in London developed penicillin? Still, many middle-class parents worried as they sat down to a Sunday joint of beef or lamb that the sweeping changes taking place would forever alter the old world that they had grown so accustomed to in the long-ago days of the Edwardian era.

In Bloomsbury, Berlin, Paris, and New York writers like Virginia Woolf and F. Scott Fitzgerald were challenging literary conventions to give voice to the "Lost Generation" of the post-War '20s.

The Jazz Age

The winds of change could also be heard emanating from the horns of a new breed of musician – the jazz player. Originating in the African-American community of New Orleans around the turn of the century, jazz not only reflected the sprit of

the '20s, it helped to define the unique character of the decade throughout the western world.

the Savoy Orpheans, blew out the walls of the stately ballroom with a driving mixture of American, Caribbean, and British spins on jazz.

Among the artists entertaining at the Savoy was a bright, suave saxophonist from New England named Rudy Valle. Leaving the Savoy band in 1925, Valle became one of the most popular bandleaders of the decade, thanks to songs like the hit "Lover Come Back To Me".

With its freedom from convention and its inspired distortions of musical tradition, jazz fit perfectly into the cultural climate of the '20s. Indeed, if jazz didn't exist before this decade began, the freewheeling tempo of the times would have led some musical genius somewhere to "invent" it. African-American artists like Fats Waller ("Ain't Misbehavin'") and the great Louis Armstrong, whose many hits of the time included "If I Could Be With You (One Hour Tonight)", helped to popularise jazz in Europe during the '20s, sparking a love affair that would flourish for the remainder of the 20th century and beyond.

The crowds that came to the Savoy in the 1920s were there to dance, as well as to listen, to the music. Dance took on a new, more personal, and perhaps more liberating dimension in the years that followed the war. When young Mr. Valle looked out over the Savoy dance floor, he would see couples jitterbugging and fox-trotting in ways that any self-respecting Edwardian would have found scandalous.

Europe, particularly Great Britain, also swung to its own home-grown jazz talent in the 1920s. Perhaps the centre of British pop music at the time was London's Savoy Hotel, where bands like the London Savoy Havana Orchestra and

Conventions and authority were being challenged as never before in the '20s on the dance floor, in the publishing house, and on the streets. The General Strike of 1926 brought London to a standstill and was a watershed event in British labour relations.

Freewheeling Pop Music

Perhaps to slow down the profound changes swirling all around them, the people of Britain – like their contemporaries in other nations – eagerly sought out harmless, innocent diversions. The decade that brought forth the dark and brooding novels of Franz Kafka also gave us Winnie the Pooh and the first Agatha

Christie mystery. Dame Agatha launched her career in 1920 with the publication of *The Mysterious Affair At Styles*, introducing the world to her engaging and eccentric detective Hercule Poirot.

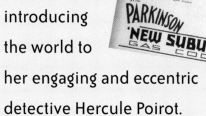

A similar pattern of edgy originality, balanced by cheerful entertainment, was also evident in the world of music. While jazz was challenging conventional standards, other popular music of the '20s was offering people a simpler diversion. Among the biggest hits in Europe were upbeat, high-energy songs with a decidedly humorous spin such as "California Here I Come", "Carolina In The Morning", "Tip Toe Through The Tulips", and "Yes Sir, That's My Baby".

Among the most enduringly popular songs to emerge from the 1920s in Europe and North America was "Someone To Watch Over Me". Written by George and Ira Gershwin, this heartfelt ballad has been recorded by major artists in every decade since its release. A frequent visitor to Europe, where he came to meet with the likes of Ravel and Poulenc, George Gershwin drew large crowds of appreciative fans when he toured London, Paris, and other cities.

New Technologies

The popular music connections between Europe and America grew stronger in the 1920s thanks, at least in part, to the advent of two new technologies: radio and talking film.

Although Guglielmo Marconi had invented his wireless machine and broadcast the world's first radio transmission from Cornwall in December 1901, radio did not arrive as a popular media outlet until the '20s. In America, KDKA (Pittsburgh) became the world's first commercial station in 1920. The British Broadcasting Corporation initiated daily broadcasts on November 14, 1922. With powerful radio stations ready to broadcast their music, stars like bandleader Paul Whiteman ("Birth Of The Blues", "Limehouse Blues", and "Oh Lady Be Good") were able to establish large and loyal fan followings on both sides of the Atlantic. A member of a band in the US Navy during the war, Whiteman formed his first band in San Francisco in 1918. At the time, jazz was performed by small combos. Whiteman's innovation was to bring the new musical genre to a larger, more lavish orchestra.

During the 1920s, Whiteman's band was one of the most popular in the US and Europe. He led his band on a wildly successful tour of the UK in 1923, adding more impetus to the growth of jazz among British fans.

The arrival of "talkies," motion pictures with sound, also ushered in a new era in trans-Atlantic music. In 1927, Warner Bros. broke the sound barrier in film when it released *The Jazz Singer*, the first motion picture in which spoken dialogue and music were used in synchronisation with action on the screen.

Starring the famous American singer, Al Jolson, the movie became a blockbuster hit in Europe and the US. Following the success of *The Jazz Singer*, cinema owners in Europe and America rushed to outfit their establishments with sound equipment. The era of the film soundtrack had begun!

So enjoy our musical sampling from the '20s, a decade that has shaped so much of our popular culture. We think you'll agree that the ten years that brought us radio and the movie soundtrack produced some delightful music too.

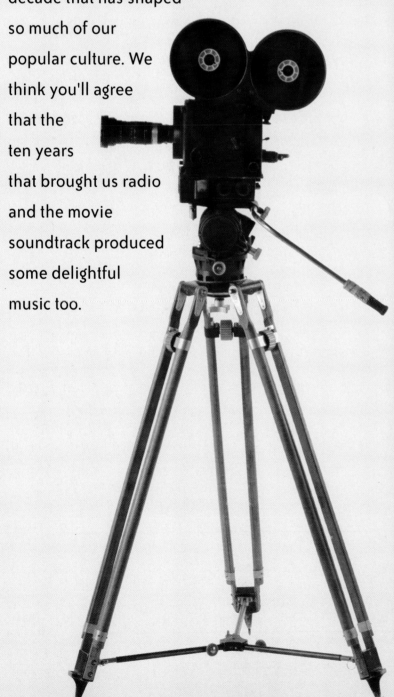

Ten Things That First Appeared In The '20s

1. The first crossword puzzle in a British newspaper (The Sunday Express, 1924).

2. One-piece radios (all earlier models required separate headsets).

3. Chanel No. 5 perfume.

4. Trans-Atlantic flight.

5. The UK's first birth control clinic (London, 1921).

6. Frozen foods.

7. Pop-up toaster.

8. Triumph cars.

9. Automatic traffic lights.

10. Winter Olympics (Charmonix, France, 1924).

ALICE BLUE GOWN

Words by JOE McCARTHY
Music by HARRY TIERNEY

AIN'T MISBEHAVIN'

Words and Music by THOMAS WALLER,
HARRY BROOKS and ANDY RAZAF

I know who I love best,
Sure was a luck - y day,

Thumbs down for all the rest,
When down fate sent you my way,

My love was giv - en, heart and soul;
And made you mine a - lone for keeps,

So it can stand the test.
Dit - to to all you say.

No one to talk to, all by my-self,

No one to walk with, but I'm hap - py on the shelf,

Ain't mis - be - ha - vin', I'm sav - in' my love for you.

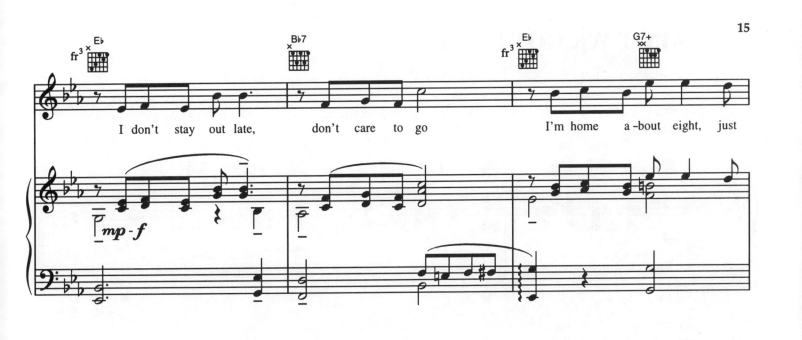

I don't stay out late, don't care to go I'm home a-bout eight, just

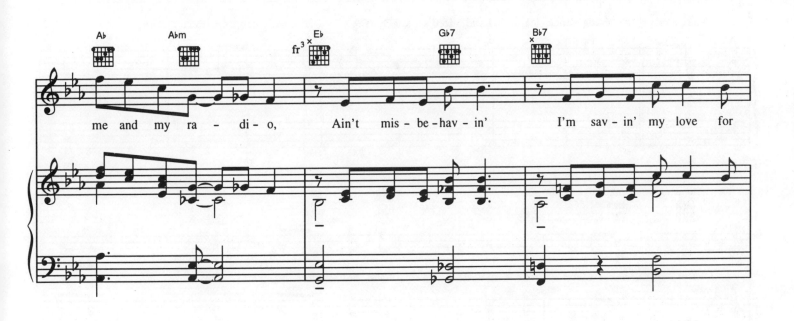

me and my ra-di-o, Ain't mis-be-hav-in' I'm sav-in' my love for

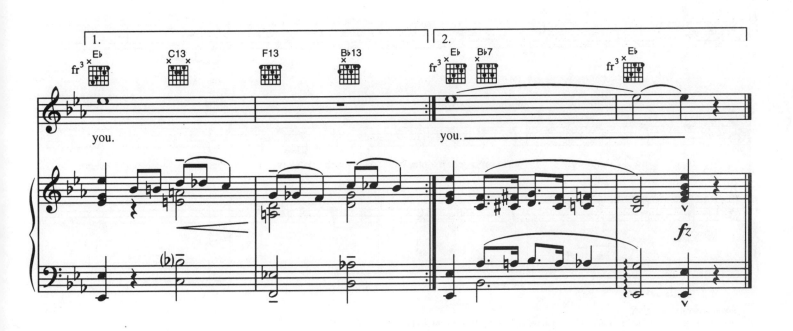

1.
you.

2.
you.

AIN'T WE GOT FUN

Words by GUS KAHN and RAYMOND B EGAN
Music by RICHARD A WHITING

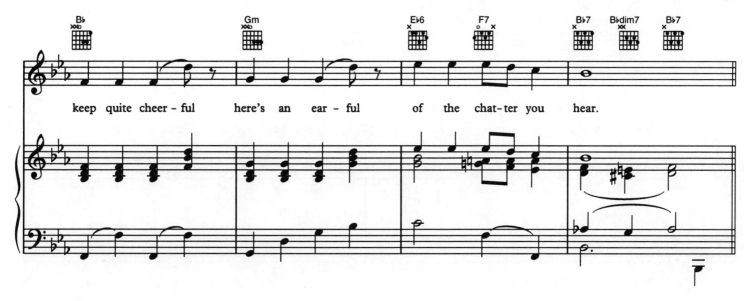

keep quite cheer-ful here's an ear-ful of the chat-ter you hear.

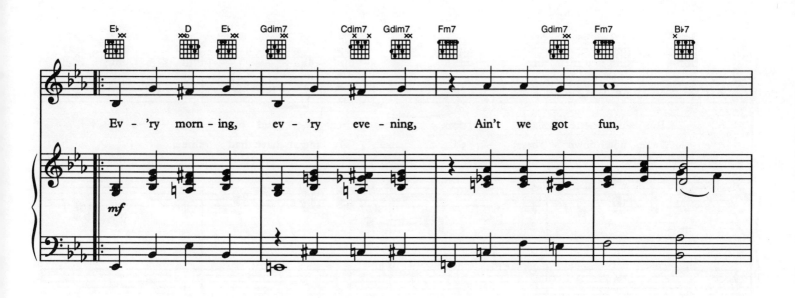

Ev-'ry morn-ing, ev-'ry eve-ning, Ain't we got fun,

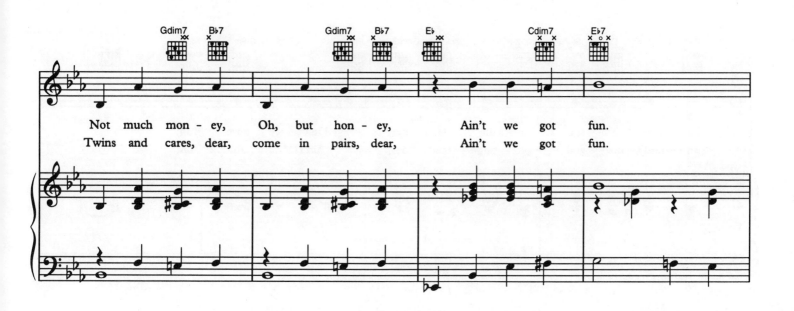

Not much mon-ey, Oh, but hon-ey, Ain't we got fun.
Twins and cares, dear, come in pairs, dear, Ain't we got fun.

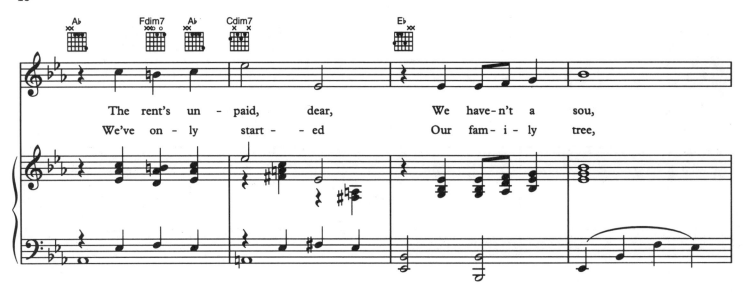

The rent's un-paid, dear,   dear,   We have-n't a sou,
We've on-ly start--ed   Our fam-i-ly tree,

But smiles were made,   dear,_____ For me and for you,
We're not down-heart - ed_____ We might have had three,

Tho' there's noth-ing   in the lar-der,   Don't we have fun;
Land-lord's mad and   get-ting mad-der,   Ain't we got fun;

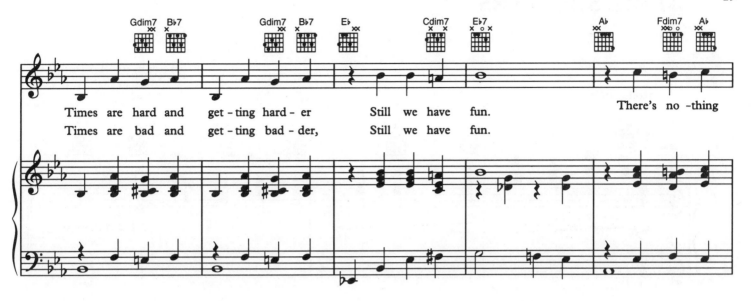

Times are hard and get-ting hard-er, Still we have fun. There's no-thing
Times are bad and get-ting bad-der, Still we have fun.

sur - er, The rich get rich and the poor get { noth - ing, In the mean - time,
{ child - ren,

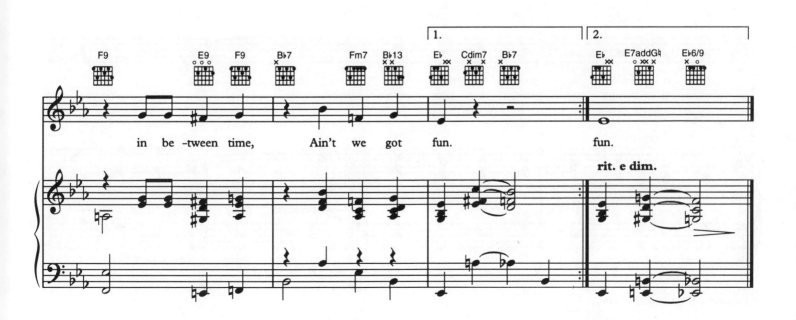

in be -tween time, Ain't we got fun. fun.

rit. e dim.

APRIL SHOWERS

Words by BUDDY De SYLVA
Music by LOUIS SILVERS

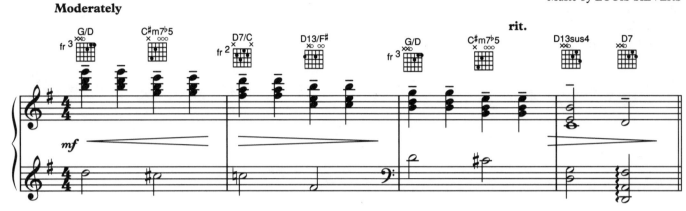

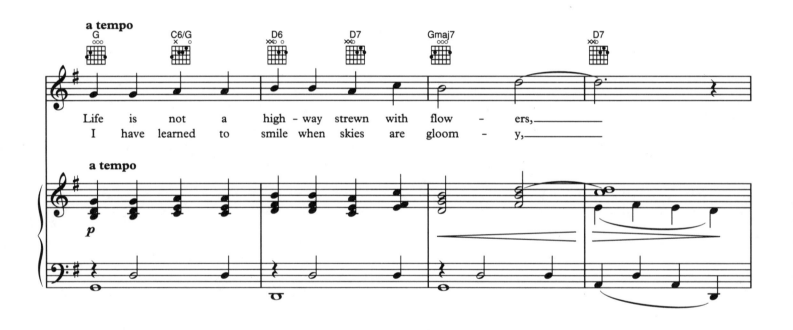

Life is not a high-way strewn with flow-ers,___
I have learned to smile when skies are gloom-y,___

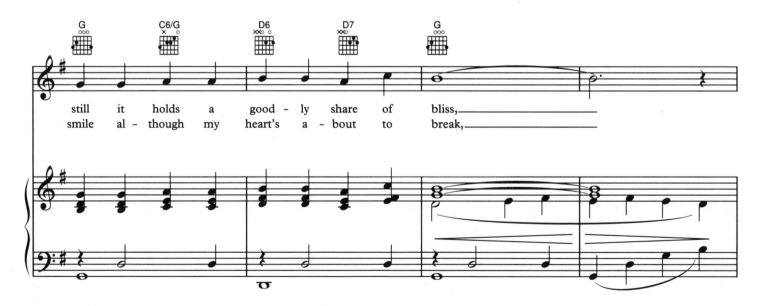

still it holds a good-ly share of bliss,___
smile al-though my heart's a-bout to break,___

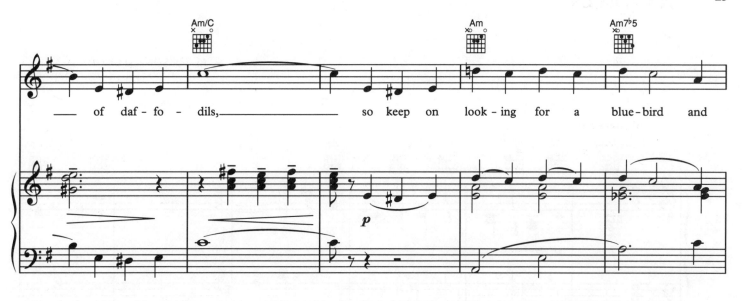

____ of daf - fo - dils, _____ so keep on look - ing for a blue - bird and

list - 'ning for his song, when - ev - er A - pril show - ers come a -

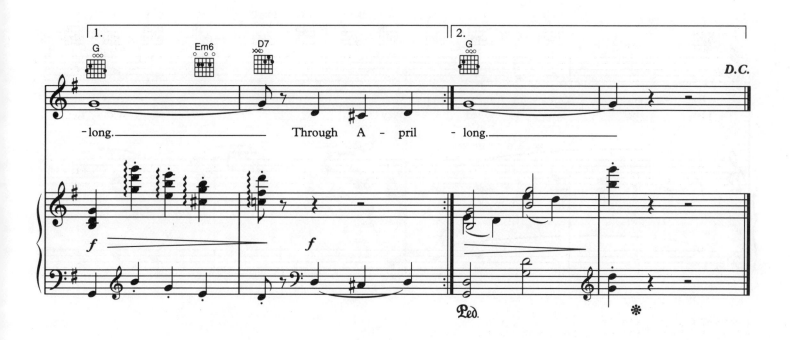

-long._____ Through A - pril -long._____

D.C.

AVALON

Words by AL JOLSON and BUDDY De SYLVA
Music by VINCENT ROSE

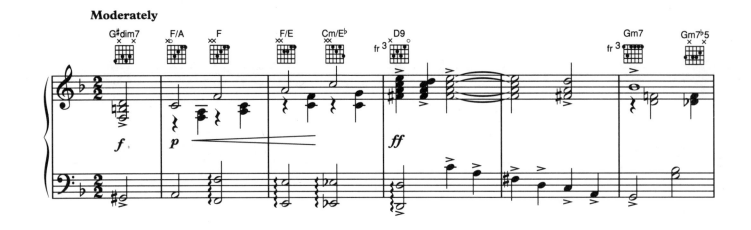

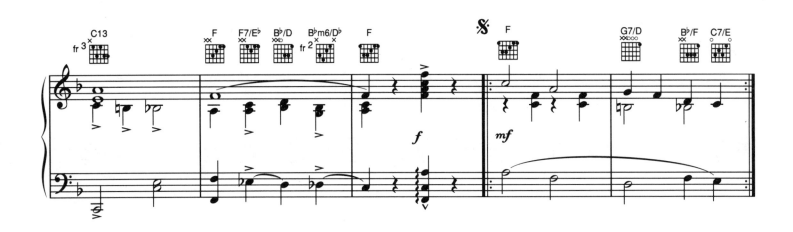

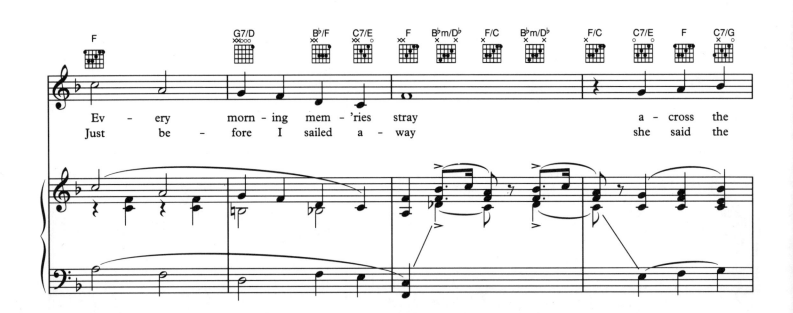

Ev - ery morn - ing mem - 'ries stray a - cross the
Just be - fore I sailed a - way she said the

BACK IN YOUR OWN BACKYARD

Words and Music by AL JOLSON, DAVE DREYER
and BILLY ROSE

THE BEST THINGS IN LIFE ARE FREE

Words and Music by BUDDY De SYLVA, LEW BROWN
and RAY HENDERSON

BLACK BOTTOM

Words by LEW BROWN and BUDDY De SYLVA
Music by RAY HENDERSON

They call it Black Bot-tom, a new twist-er; it's sure got 'em, and oh, Sis-ter: they clap their hands and do a rag-ged-y trot. Hot!

THE BIRTH OF THE BLUES

Words by BUDDY De SYLVA and LEW BROWN
Music by RAY HENDERSON

pushed it through a horn 'til it was worn___ in-to a blue___ note!___

___ And then they nursed it, re - hearsed___ it, and gave___ out the news

___ that the South - land gave birth___ to the

blues!___ They heard the blues!___

THE BLUE ROOM

Words by LORENZ HART
Music by RICHARD RODGERS

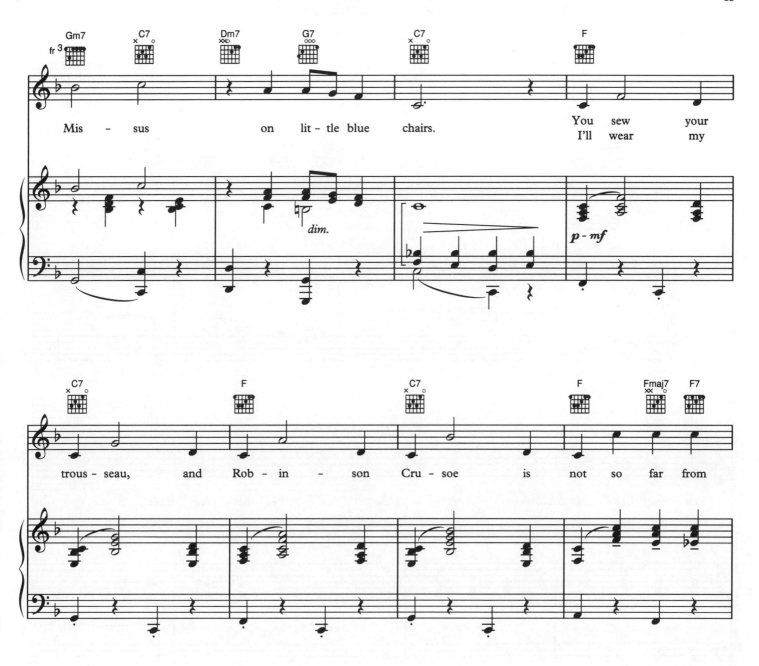

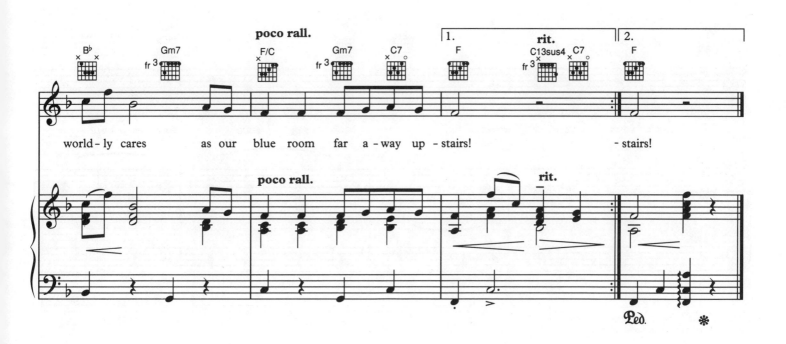

BUTTON UP YOUR OVERCOAT

Words and Music by B G DeSYLVA,
LEW BROWN and RAY HENDERSON

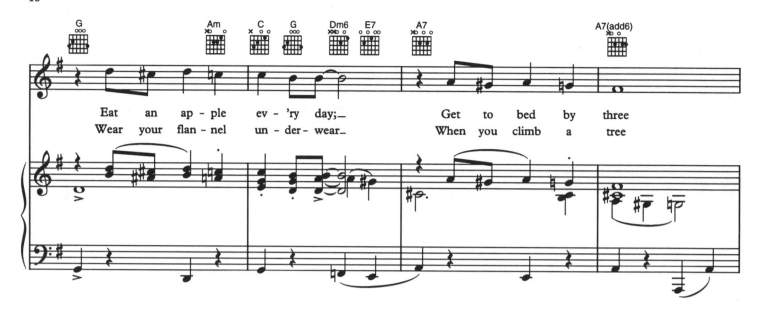

Eat an ap-ple ev-'ry day;__ Get to bed by three
Wear your flan-nel un-der-wear__ When you climb a tree

Take good__ care of your-self__ you be-long to me!_____ Be care-ful
Take good__ care of your-self__ you be-long to me!_____ Don't sit on

cross - ing streets Oo - -oo! Don't eat meats Oo - -oo!
hor - nets' tails Oo - -oo! Or on nails Oo - -oo!

BYE BYE BLACKBIRD

Words by MORT DIXON
Music by RAY HENDERSON

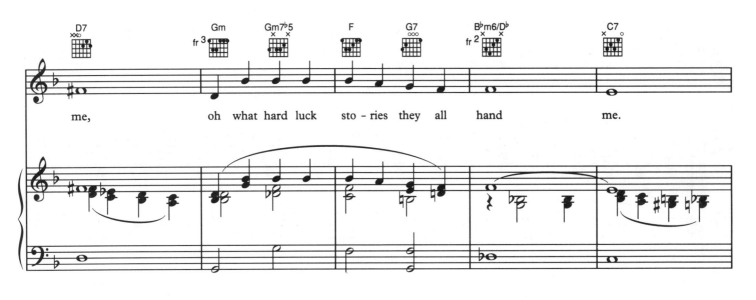

me, oh what hard luck sto-ries they all hand me.

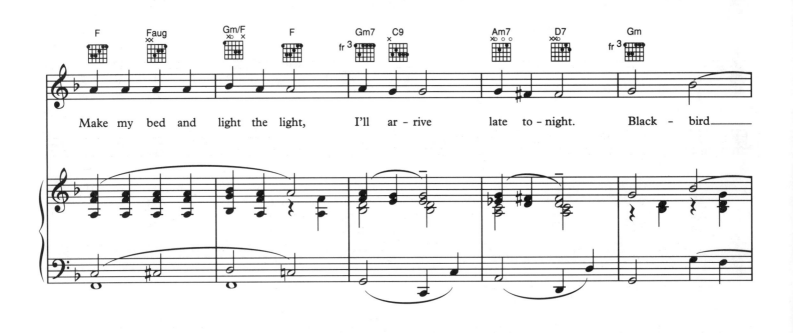

Make my bed and light the light, I'll ar-rive late to-night. Black - bird_____

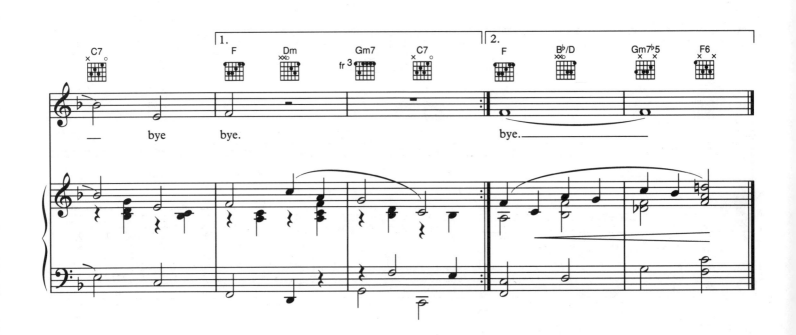

bye bye. bye._____

CAROLINA IN THE MORNING

Words by GUS KAHN
Music by WALTER DONALDSON

CALIFORNIA HERE I COME

Words and Music by AL JOLSON,
BUDDY DeSYLVA and JOSEPH MEYER

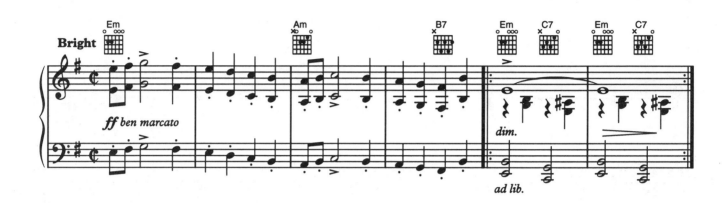

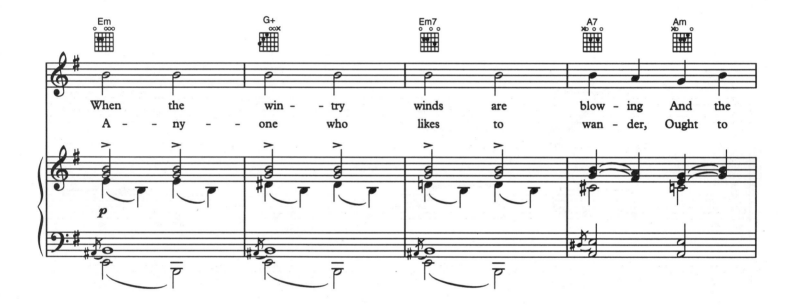

When the win-try winds are blow-ing And the
A - ny - one who likes to wan-der, Ought to

snow is start-ing in-to fall;
keep this say-ing in his mind;

sun - kiss'd miss said, "Don't be late!"___ That's why I can

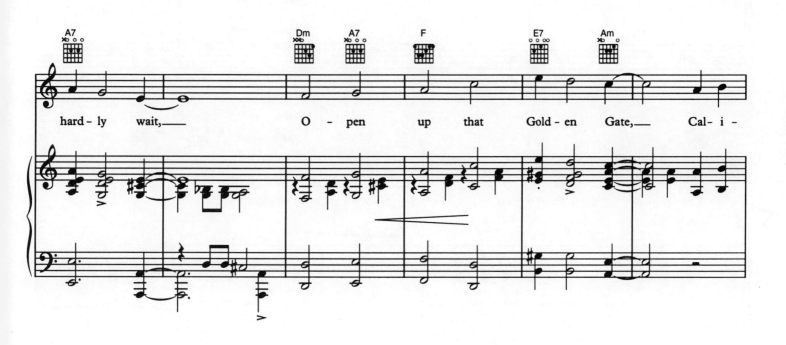

hard - ly wait,___ O - pen up that Gold - en Gate,___ Cal - i -

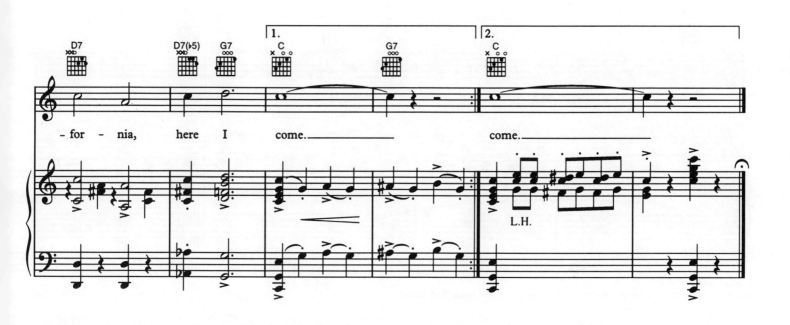

-for - nia, here I come.___ come.___

THE CHARLESTON

Words and Music by CECIL MACK
and JIMMY JOHNSON

Car - o - lin - a, Car - o - lin - a, At last they've got you on the map,

With a new tune, Fun - ny blue tune, With a pe - cu - liar snap! You may

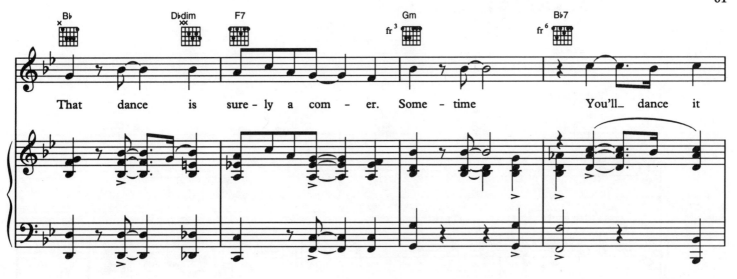

That dance is sure-ly a com - er. Some-time You'll dance it

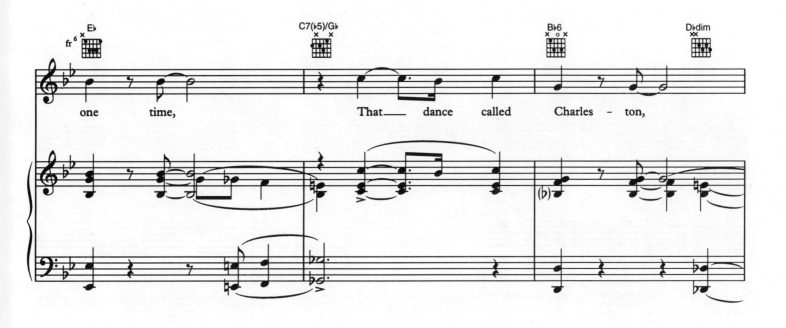

one time, That_ dance called Charles-ton,

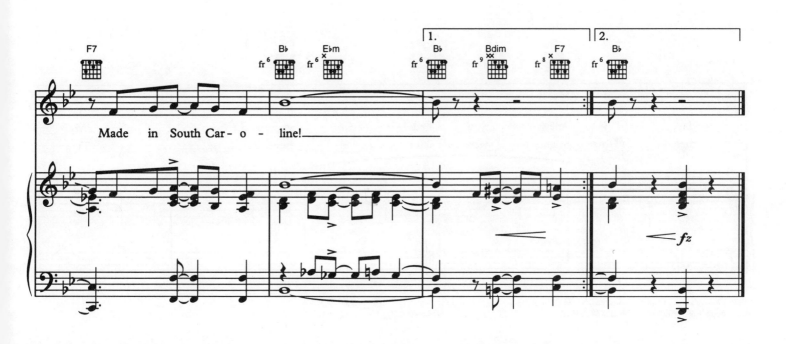

Made in South Car-o-line!_____

CHARMAINE

Words by LEW POLLACK
Music by ERNO RAPEE

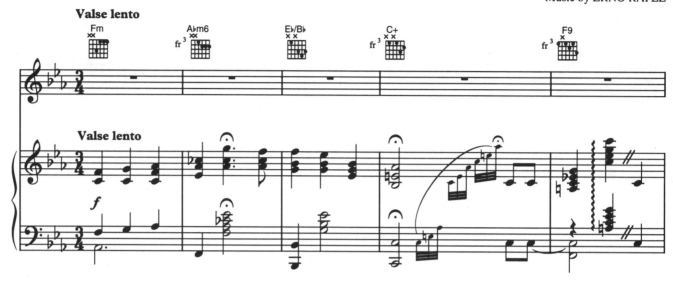

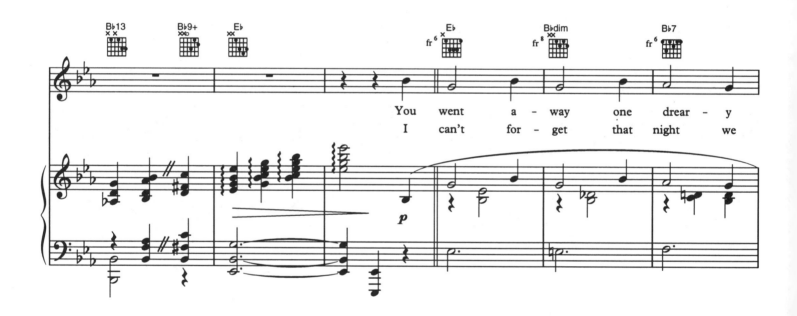

You went a - way one drear - y
I can't for - get that night we

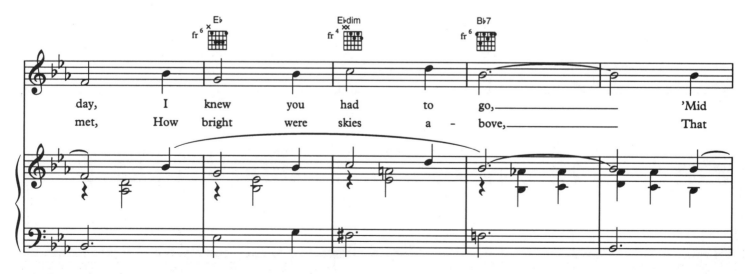

day, I knew you had to go,_____ 'Mid
met, How bright were skies a - bove,_____ That

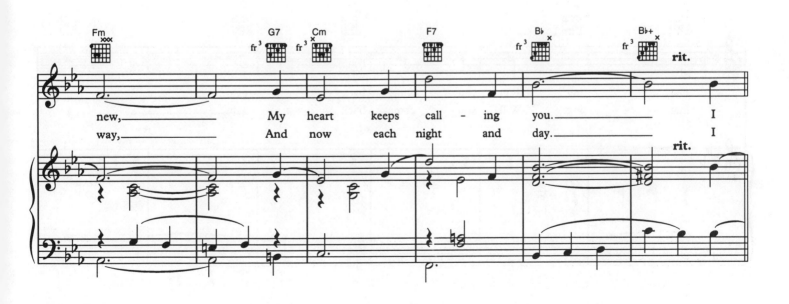

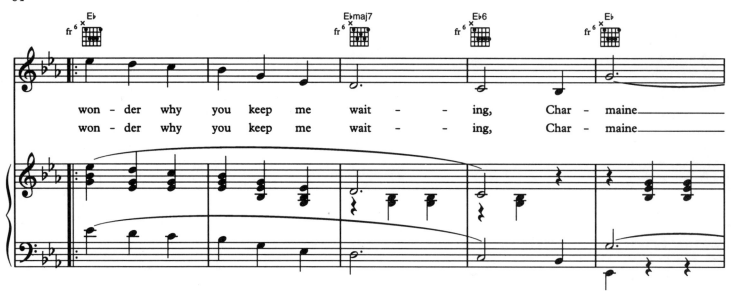

won - der why you keep me wait - - ing, Char - maine_____
won - der why you keep me wait - - ing, Char - maine_____

—— cries in vain,_____ I won - der when blue - birds are
—— my Char - maine_____ I won - der when blue - birds are

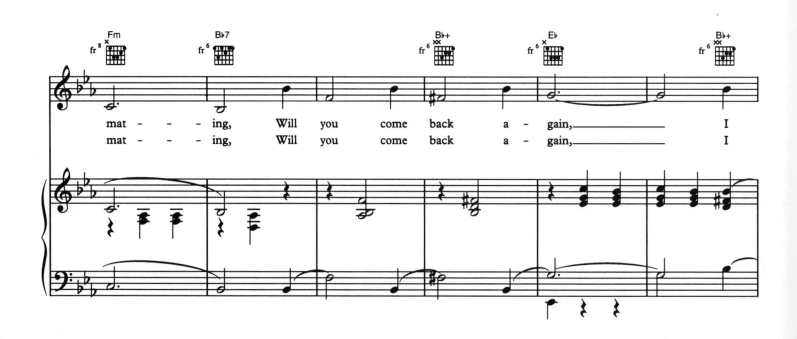

mat - - ing, Will you come back a - gain,_____ I
mat - - ing, Will you come back a - gain,_____ I

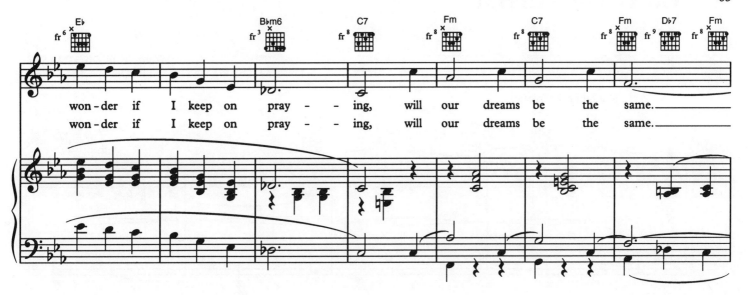

won-der if I keep on pray – – ing, will our dreams be the same.____
won-der if I keep on pray – – ing, will our dreams be the same.____

____ I won-der if ev-er you think of me, too, Char -maine's
____ I won-der if ev-er you think of me, too, I am

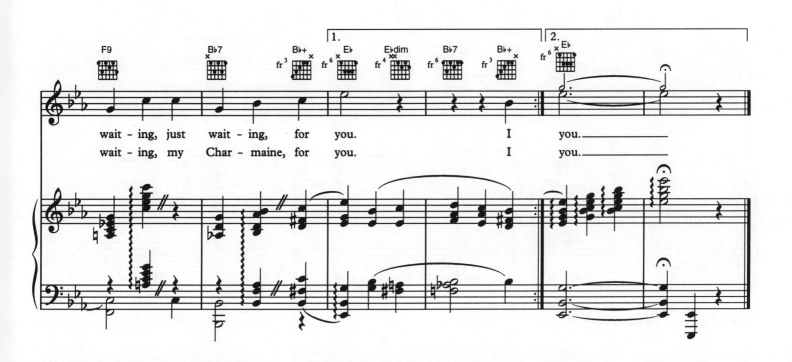

wait-ing, just wait-ing, for you. I you.____
wait-ing, my Char-maine, for you. I you.____

CRAZY RHYTHM

Words by IRVING CAESAR
Music by JOSEPH MEYER and ROGER WOLFE KAHN

Moderately lively

I feel like the Em-per-or Ne-ro when Rome was a ve-ry hot town;
Ev-'ry Greek, each Turk and each La-tin, the Russ-ians and Pruss-ians as well,

Fath-er Kni-cker-bock-er, for-give me, I play while your ci-ty burns
when they seek the lure of Man-hat-tan, are sure to come un-der your

DIANE

Words by LEW POLLACK
Music by ERNO RAPEE

DEAR LITTLE CAFE

Words and Music by NOËL COWARD

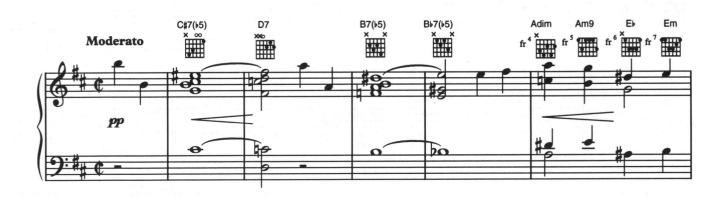

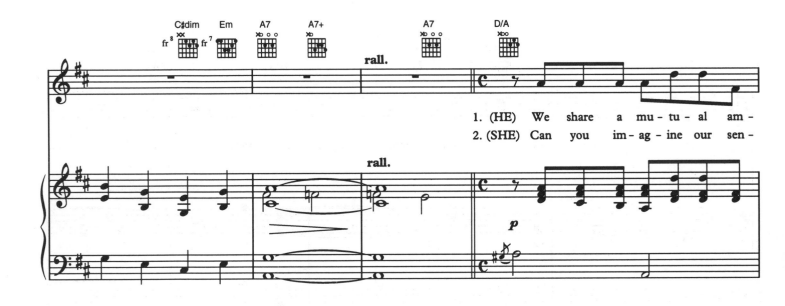

1. (HE) We share a mu-tu-al am-
2. (SHE) Can you im-ag-ine our sen-

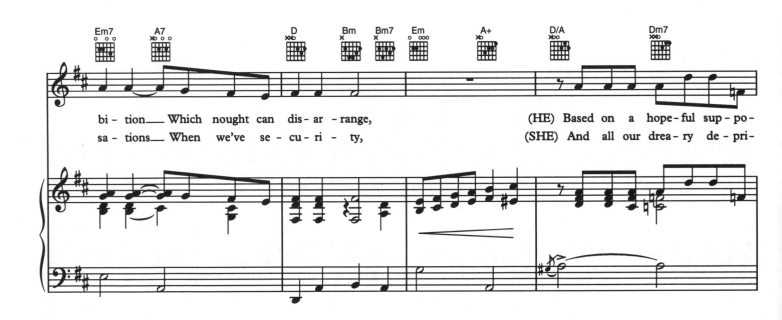

bi - tion__ Which nought can dis-ar-range,   (HE) Based on a hope-ful sup-po-
sa - tions__ When we've se-cu-ri-ty,   (SHE) And all our drea-ry de-pri-

How - ev - er hard the bed one lies on___ The same old dreams be - gin,
Fate need - n't be quite such a drag - on___ He knows how tired we are.

We're al - ways scan -ning the ho - ri - zon___ For when our ship comes in.___
We'll hitch our hope - ful lit - tle wag - on,___ On - to a luck - y star.___ We'll have a

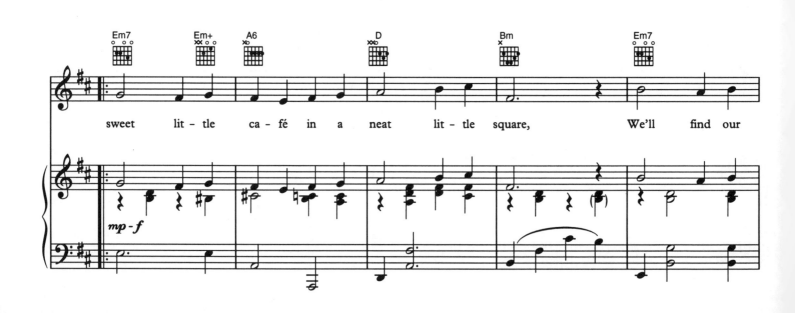

sweet lit - tle ca - fé in a neat lit - tle square, We'll find our

for - tune and our hap - pi - ness there. We shall thrive on the vain and re -

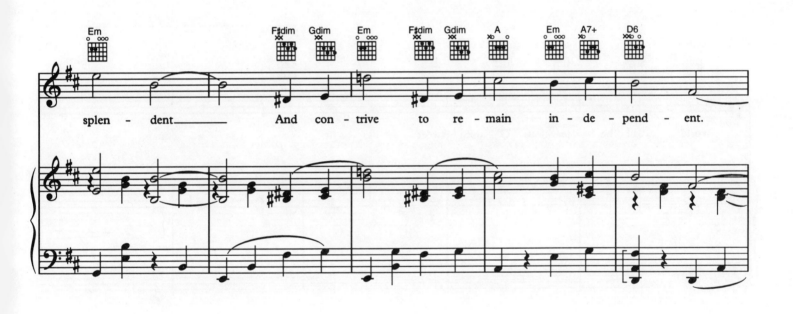

splen - dent_____ And con - trive to re - main in - de - pend - ent.

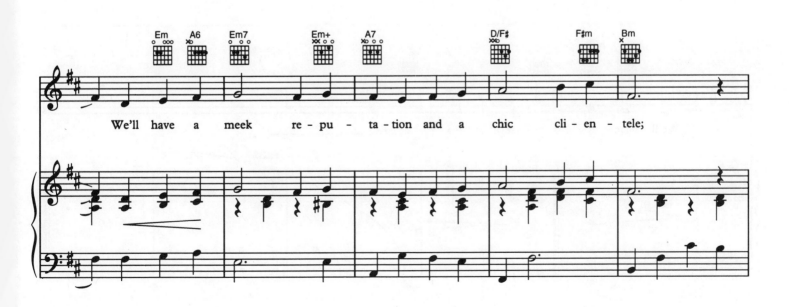

We'll have a meek re - pu - ta - tion and a chic cli - en - tele;

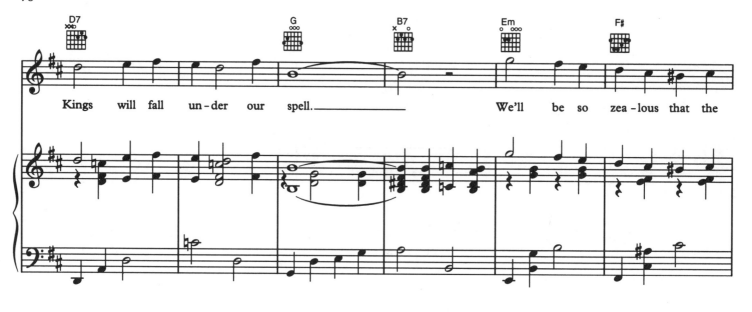

Kings will fall un-der our spell._____ We'll be so zea-lous that the

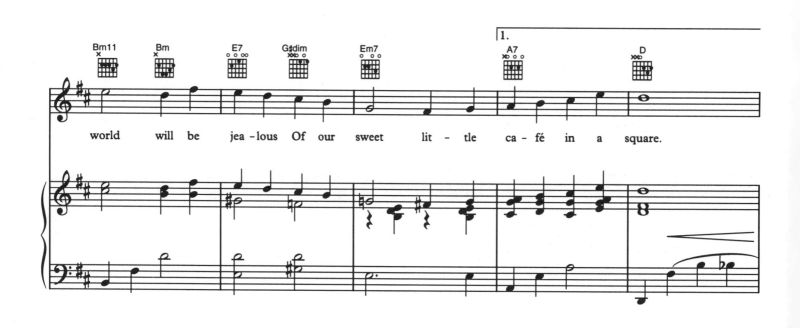

world will be jea-lous Of our sweet lit-tle ca-fé in a square.

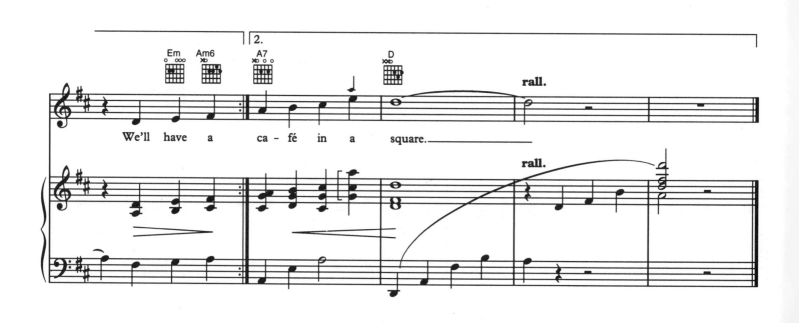

We'll have a ca-fé in a square._____

HALLELUJAH

Words by LEO ROBIN and CLIFFORD GREY
Music by VINCENT YOUMANS

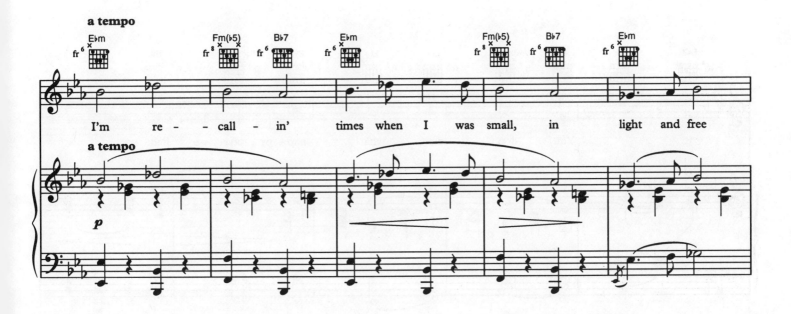

I'm re-call-in' times when I was small, in light and free

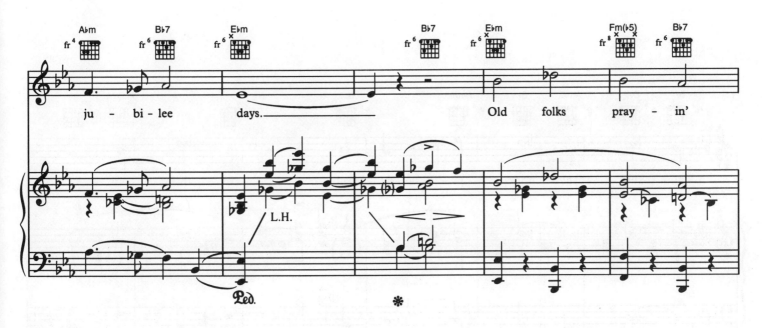

ju-bi-lee days. _____ Old folks pray-in'

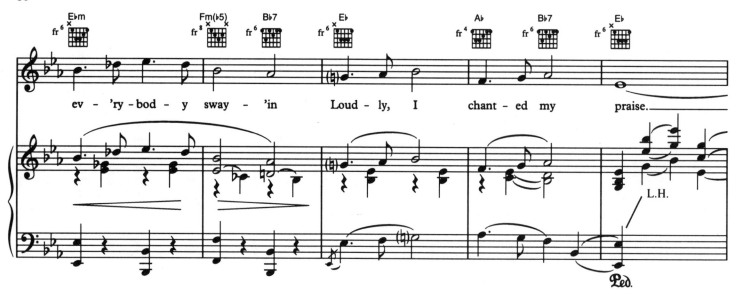

ev - 'ry - bod - y sway - 'in Loud - ly, I chant - ed my praise.

You don't know what hap - py days we had.

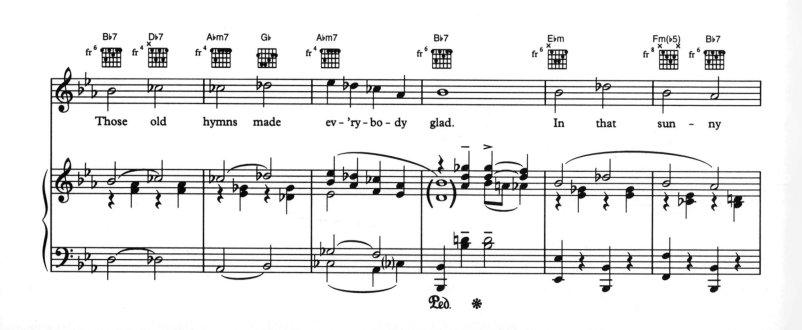

Those old hymns made ev - 'ry - bo - dy glad. In that sun - ny

land of milk and hon - ey, I had no com -plaints While I thought of

saints, So I say to all who may be sad:_____ Sing "Hal - le -

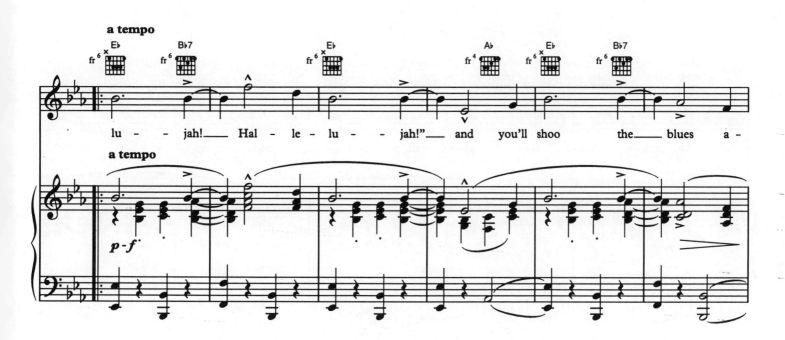

lu - - jah!____ Hal - le - lu - - jah!"____ and you'll shoo the____ blues a -

way._____ When cares pur - sue ya,___ "Hal - le - lu - - jah"___

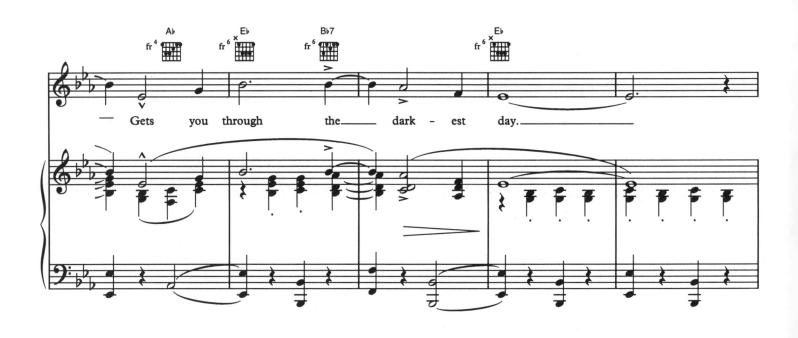

__ Gets you through the__ dark - est day._____

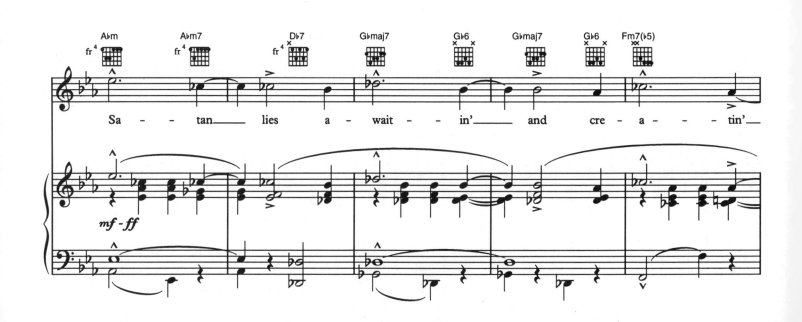

Sa - tan__ lies a - wait - - in'__ and cre - a - - tin'__

HAPPY DAYS ARE HERE AGAIN

Words by JACK YELLEN
Music by MILTON AGER

So long, sad times! Go 'long,
No more sigh - ing, No more

bad times! We are rid of you at last.
cry - ing, Clouds of grey have turned to blue.

How - dy, gay times! Clou - dy grey times,
Sor - row fly - ing, cares de - ny - ing,

I CRIED FOR YOU

Words and Music by ARTHUR FREED,
GUS ARNHEIM and ABE LYMAN

1. I re - mem - ber
2. How can I for -

oth - er days   how I used to weep   O - ver things you said to me
get the hours   that I wor - ried through   Won - der - ing the live - long day

found a heart just a lit – tle bit tru – – er   I   cried____

____ for you____   Now it's your turn to cry o – – ver

me.____   me.____

I LOVE MY BABY

Words by BUD GREEN
Music by HARRY WARREN

And may - be we fight / But then we make up
She's learn - ing to bake / I like her cof - fee

The fol - low - ing night / When we're to - geth - er we're
It keeps us a - wake / We wash the dish - es from

great com - pa - ny____ / I love my ba - by
se - ven to three____ / My ba - by loves

1.
me.____

2.
me.____

I'M LOOKING OVER A FOUR LEAF CLOVER

Words by MORT DIXON
Music by HARRY WOODS

I WANT TO BE HAPPY

Words by IRVING CAESAR
Music by VINCENT YOUMANS

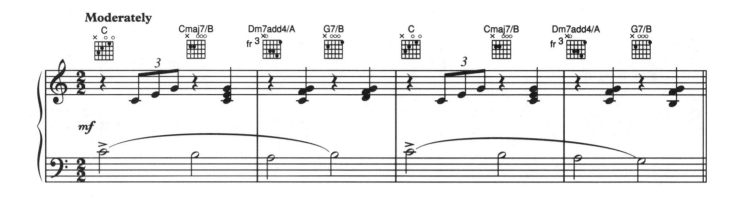

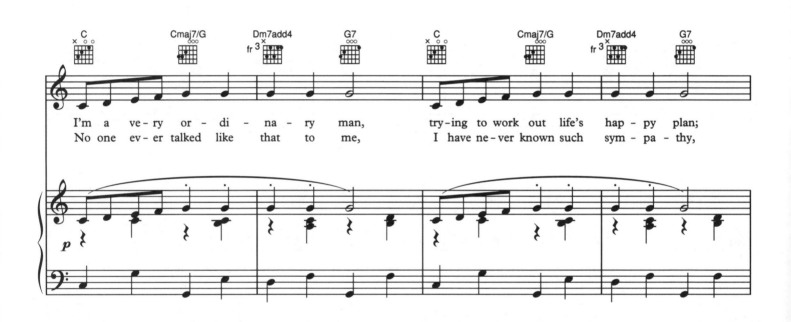

I'm a ve-ry or-di-na-ry man, try-ing to work out life's hap-py plan;
No one ev-er talked like that to me, I have ne-ver known such sym-pa-thy,

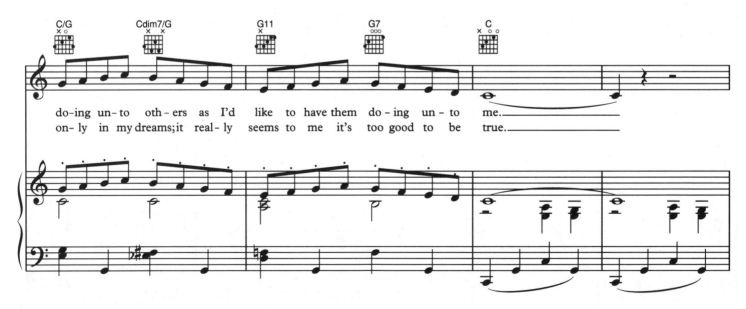

do-ing un-to oth-ers as I'd like to have them do-ing un-to me.
on-ly in my dreams; it real-ly seems to me it's too good to be true.

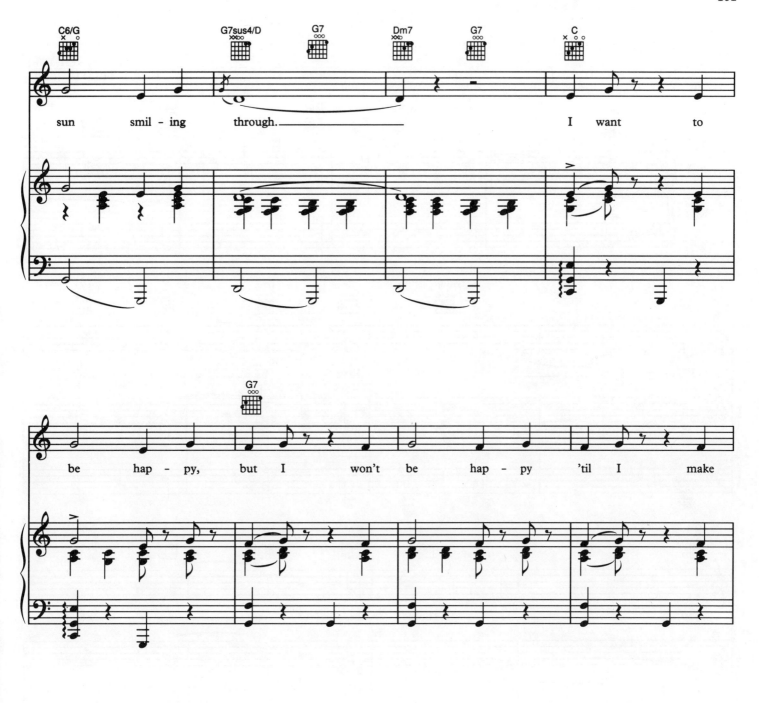

sun smil - ing through._____ I want to

be hap - py, but I won't be hap - py 'til I make

you hap - py too! too!_____

I'LL GET BY

Words by ROY TURK
Music by FRED E AHLERT

I'LL SEE YOU AGAIN

Words and Music by NOËL COWARD

To be-gin with, if you please, sing a scale for me. Take a breath and then re - prise in a diff-'rent key. All my life I shall re-mem-ber

I'LL SEE YOU IN MY DREAMS

Words by GUS KAHN
Music by ISHAM JONES

1. Though the days are long,
2. In the drea-ry grey,

Twi-light sings a song, Of the hap-pi-ness that used to be;
Of an-oth-er day, You'll be far a-way and I'll be blue;

Soon my eyes will close. Soon I'll find re - pose,
Still I hope and pray, Through each wea - ry day,

And in dreams you're al - ways near to me._____
For it brings the night and dreams of you._____

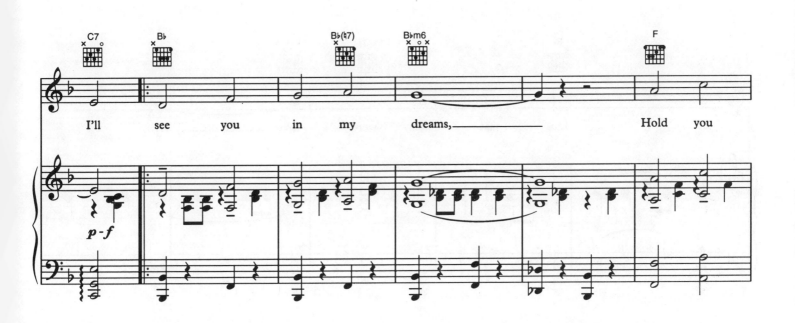

I'll see you in my dreams,_____ Hold you

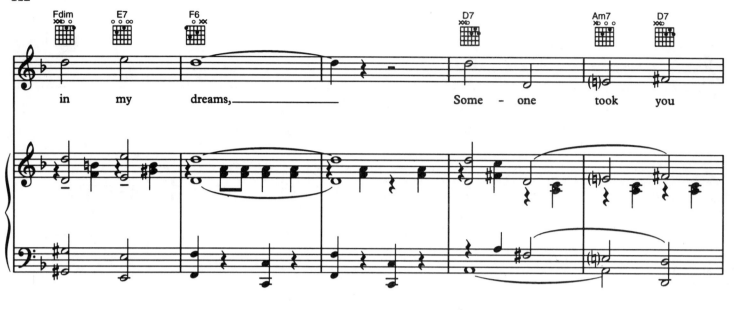

in my dreams,_____ Some - one took you

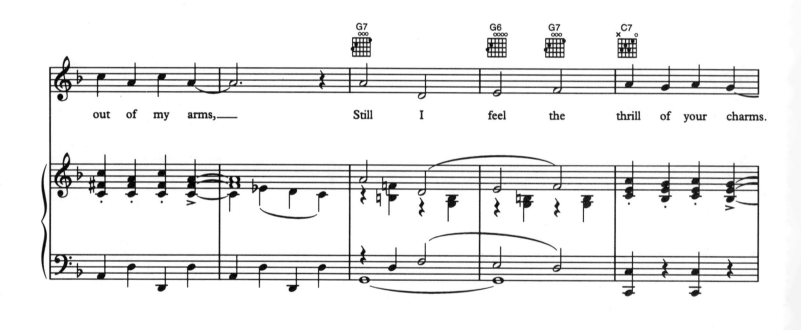

out of my arms,___ Still I feel the thrill of your charms.

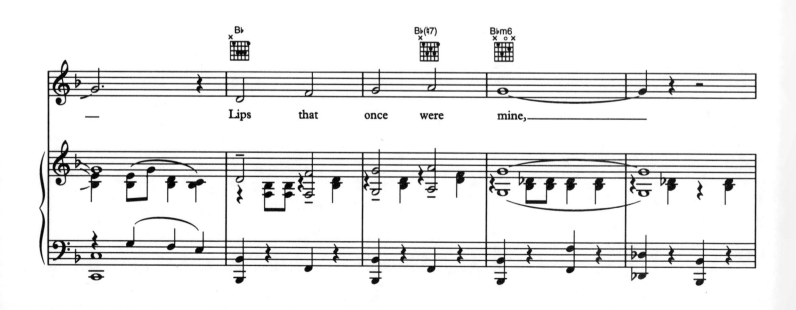

— Lips that once were mine,_____

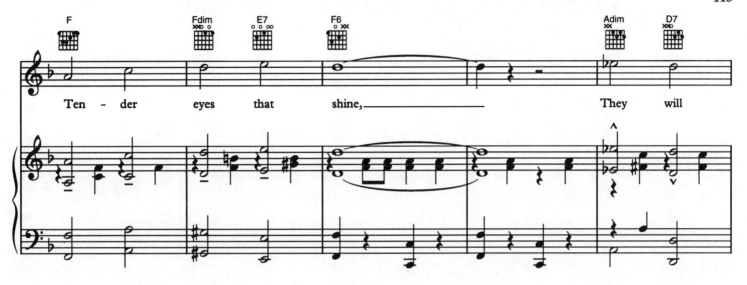

Ten - der eyes that shine,_____ They will

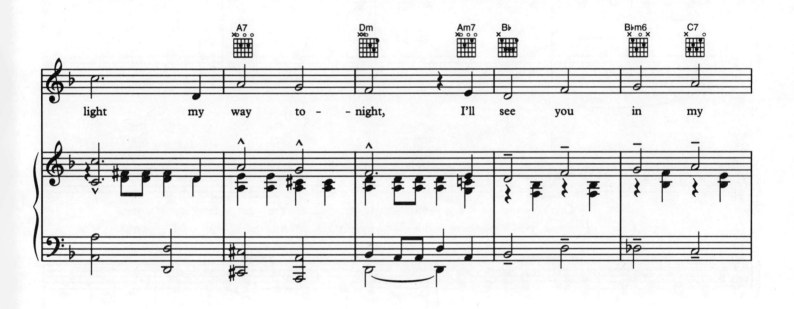

light my way to - -night, I'll see you in my

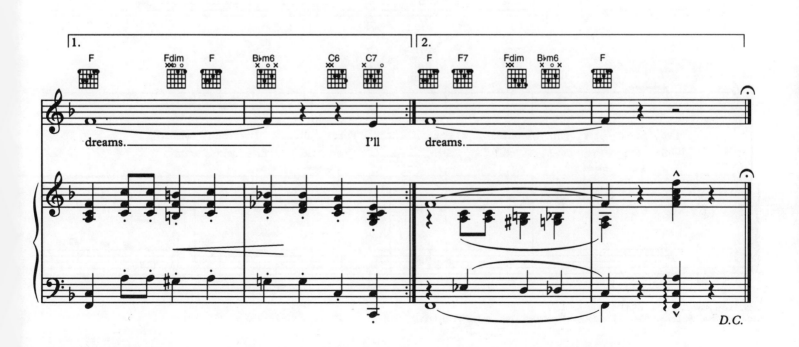

dreams._____ I'll dreams._____

D.C.

I'M SITTING ON TOP OF THE WORLD

Words by SAM LEWIS and JOE YOUNG
Music by RAY HENDERSON

Don't want an-y mil-lions,_____ I'm get-ting my share;
Some peo-ple have dia-monds_____ And beau-ti-ful pearls,

I've on-ly got one suit,_____ That's all_____ I can wear.
While oth-ers have chil-dren,_____ Just kid-dies with curls.

fall.   I'm sit-ting   on top of   the world,   Just roll-ing a-

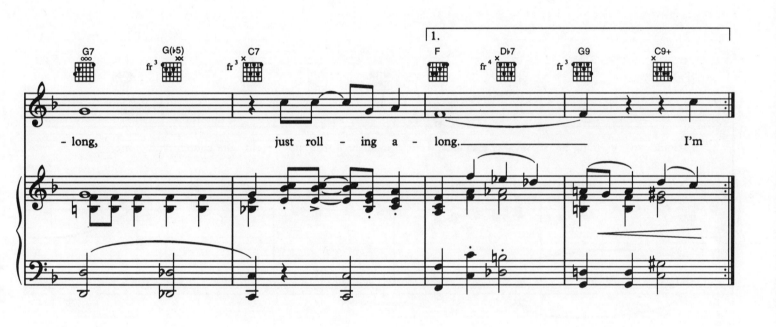

-long,   just roll-ing a-long._____   I'm

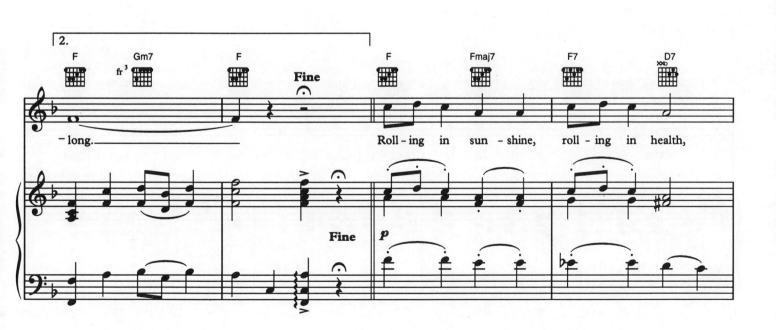

-long._____   Roll-ing in sun-shine,   roll-ing in health,

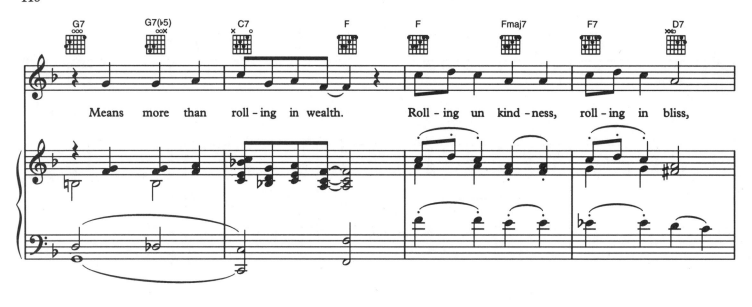

Means more than roll-ing in wealth. Roll-ing un kind-ness, roll-ing in bliss,

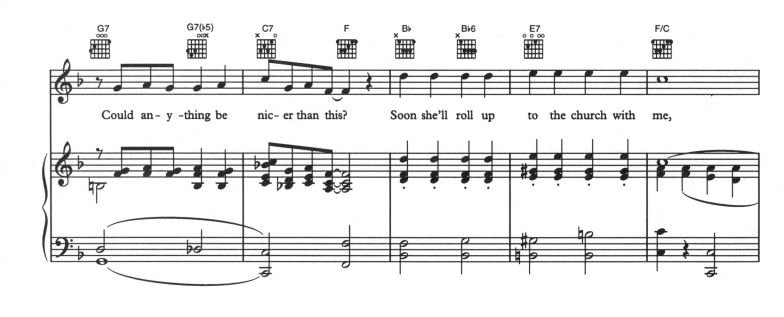

Could an-y-thing be nic-er than this? Soon she'll roll up to the church with me,

D.S. al Fine 𝄋

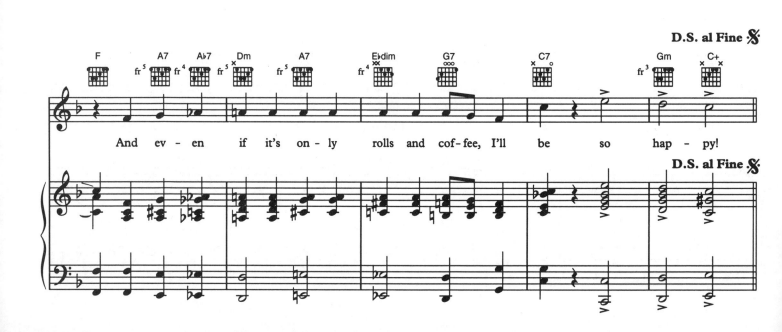

And ev-en if it's on-ly rolls and cof-fee, I'll be so hap-py!

D.S. al Fine 𝄋

IF LOVE WERE ALL

Words and Music by NOËL COWARD

Life is ve-ry rough and tum-ble For a hum-ble dis-euse;
Tho' life buf-fets me ob-scene-ly It se-rene-ly goes on;

One can be-tray one's trou-bles nev-er What-ev-er oc-curs.
Al-tho' I ques-tion its con-clu-sion, Il-lu-sion is gone.

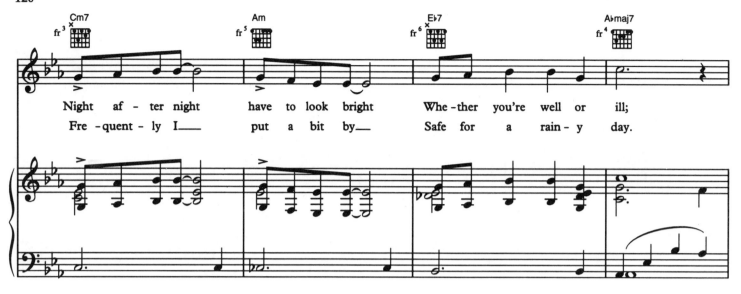

Night af - ter night have to look bright Whe -ther you're well or ill;
Fre -quent - ly I___ put a bit by___ Safe for a rain - y day.

Peo -ple must laugh their fill.___ You must - n't sleep___ till dawn comes creep - ing.
No - bo - dy here can say___ To what in - deed___ the years are lead - ing.

Tho' I nev - er real - ly grum - ble Life's a jum - ble in - deed,___
Fate may of - ten treat me mean - ly, But I keen - ly pur - sue___

And in my ef-forts to suc- ceed_____ I've had to form - u - late a creed._____
— A lit- tle mi-rage in the blue._____ De - ter-min - a - tion helps me through.—

I be -lieve in do-ing what I can, In cry-ing when I must in laugh-ing when I chose.

Heigh - o,_____ If love were all_____ I should be lone - ly. I be -lieve the

more you love a man, The more you give your trust, The more you're bound to lose: Al – though __

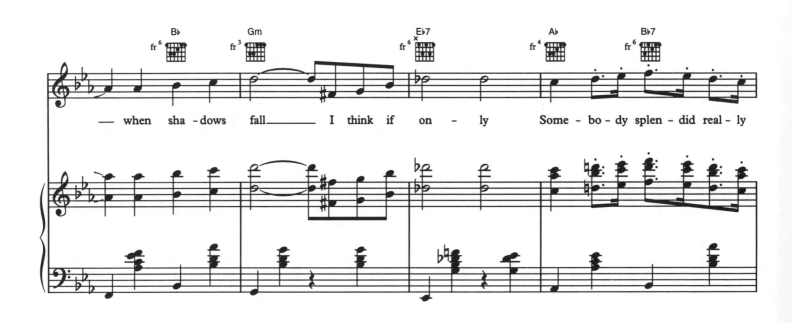

__ when sha – dows fall __ I think if on – ly Some – bo – dy splen – did real – ly

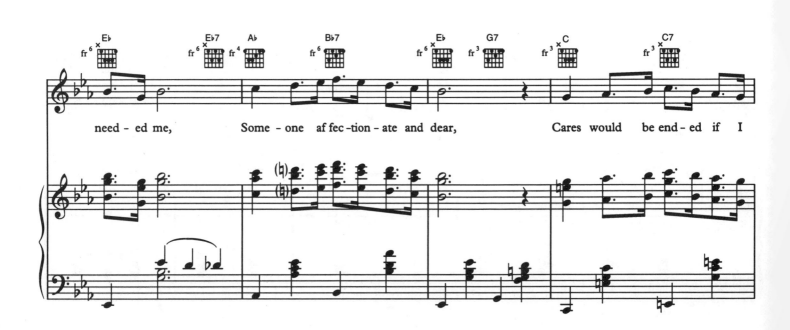

need – ed me, Some – one af fec – tion – ate and dear, Cares would be end – ed if I

knew that he Want – ed to have me near. But I be – lieve that

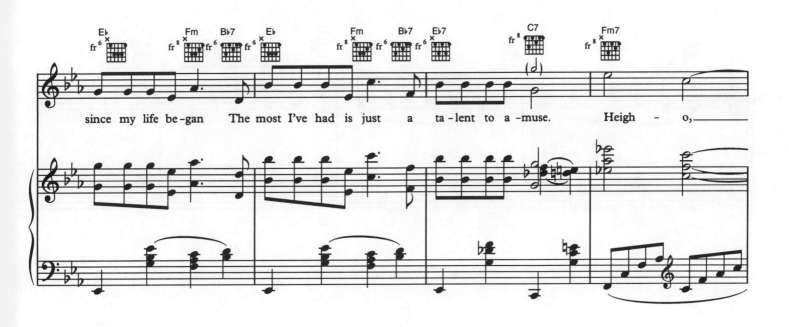

since my life be – gan The most I've had is just a ta – lent to a –muse. Heigh – o,___

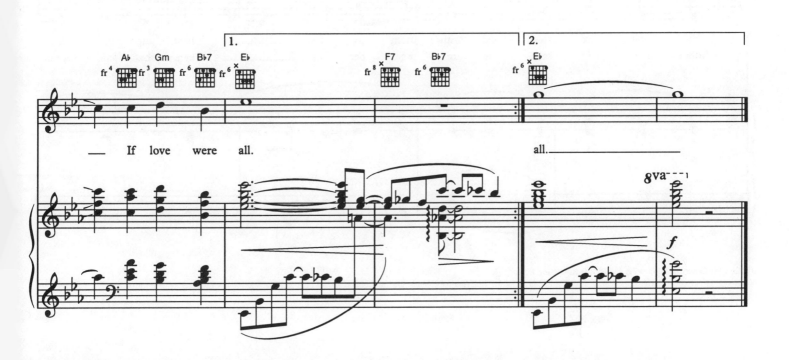

___ If love were all. all.___

IN A LITTLE SPANISH TOWN

Words and Music by SAM LEWIS,
JOE YOUNG and MABEL WAYNE

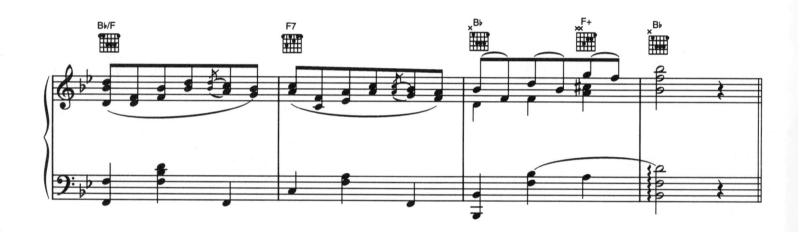

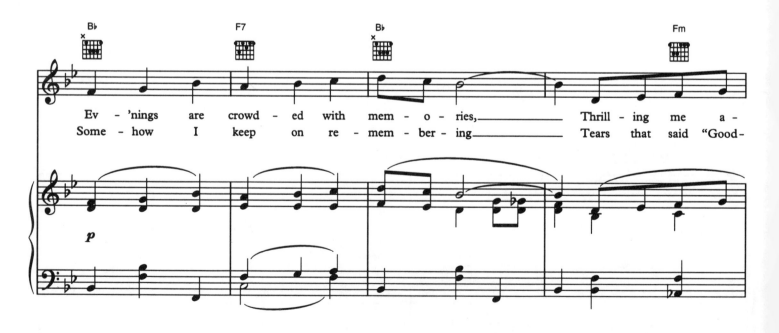

Ev - 'nings are crowd - ed with mem - o - ries,_____ Thrill - ing me a -
Some - how I keep on re - mem - ber - ing_____ Tears that said "Good-

- gain,_____ Like that night in Spain._____
- bye,"_____ Shin - ing in her eye._____

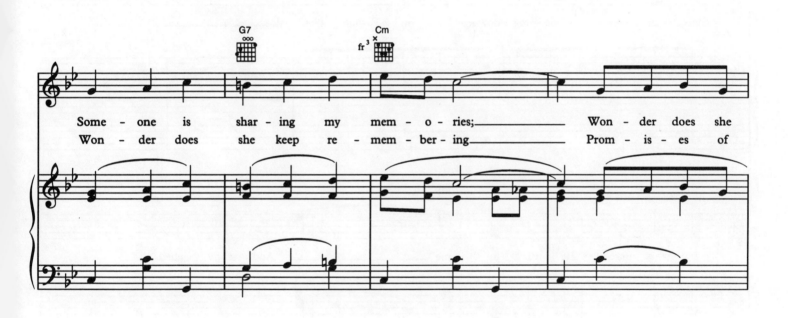

Some - one is shar - ing my mem - o - ries;_____ Won - der does she
Won - der does she keep re - mem - ber - ing_____ Prom - is - es of

grieve_____ Ev - 'ry love - ly ev - - 'ning.
mine,_____ When the moon is shin - - - ing?

IT ALL DEPENDS ON YOU

Words by LEW BROWN and BUDDY DeSYLVA
Music by RAY HENDERSON

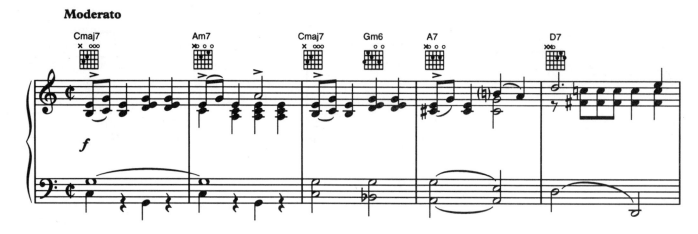

Lov - ers de - pend on moon - light For a love af - fair.
Is - n't it sweet to know, dear, You can help me on.

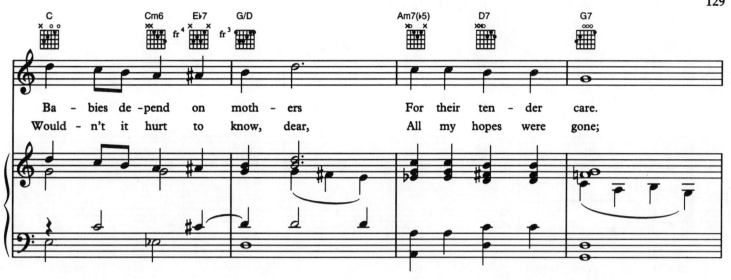

Ba – bies de –pend on moth – ers   For their ten – der care.
Would – n't it hurt to know, dear,   All my hopes were gone;

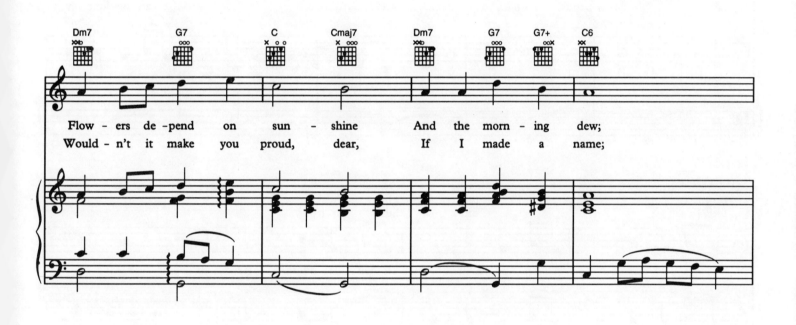

Flow – ers de –pend on sun – shine   And the morn – ing dew;
Would – n't it make you proud, dear,   If I made a name;

Each thing de –pends on some – thing,   And I de –pend on you.
But if I failed to win, dear,   Would you want all the blame?

IN A SHADY NOOK BY A BABBLING BROOK

Words by HARRY PEASE
Music by ED G NELSON

JEALOUSY

Words by WINIFRED MAY
Music by JACOB GADE

LET ME SING AND I'M HAPPY

Words and Music by IRVING BERLIN

For the world's af - fairs? As long as I can sing its pop - u - lar
That my song's ap - peal Has reached your hearts, I'll not ask an - y - thing

songs._____
more._____

Let me sing_ a fun - ny song, with cra - zy words that

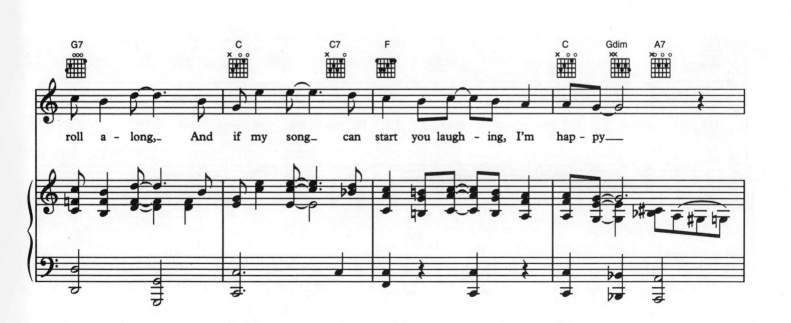

roll a - long,_ And if my song_ can start you laugh - ing, I'm hap - py_

hap - py.___ Let me sing a sad re - frain, of brok - en hearts that

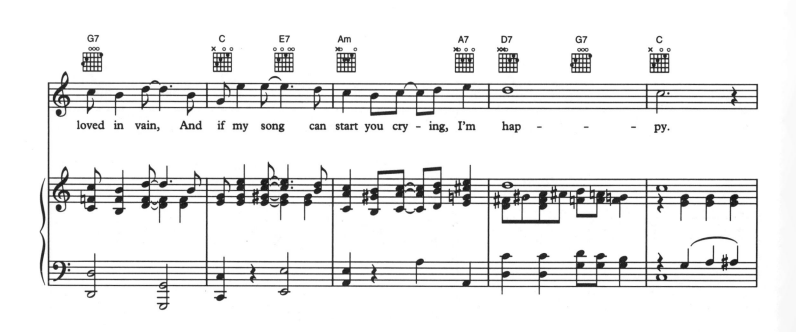

loved in vain, And if my song can start you cry - ing, I'm hap - - - py.

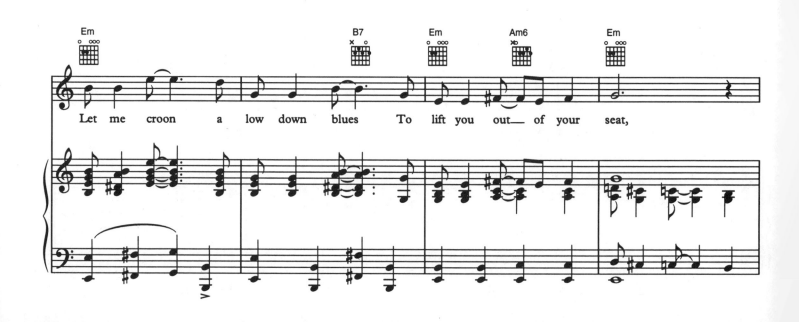

Let me croon a low down blues To lift you out___ of your seat,

If my song can reach your shoes and start you tap - ping your feet, I'm hap - py. Let me sing of

Dix - ie's charms, of cot - ton fields and Mam - my's arms, And if my song can make you home - sick, I'm

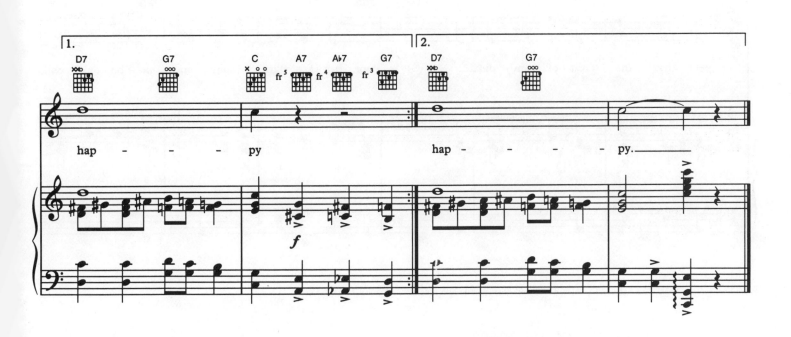

hap - - - py   hap - - - py._____

LIMEHOUSE BLUES

Words by DOUGLAS FURBER
Music by PHILIP BRAHAM

Oh! Lime-house kid___ Oh! Oh! Oh! Lime-house kid___ Go - ing the way ___ that the rest of them did___ Poor Bro-ken Blos - som and no-bo-dy's child

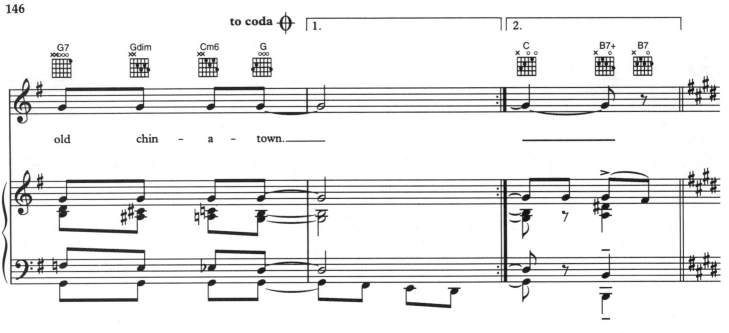

old   chin - a - town._____

In_____   Lime - - - house
Oh_____   Dear - - - ie

where   all   the   Chin - ese   love   to   play_____
right   here   in   or - ange   blos - som   land_____

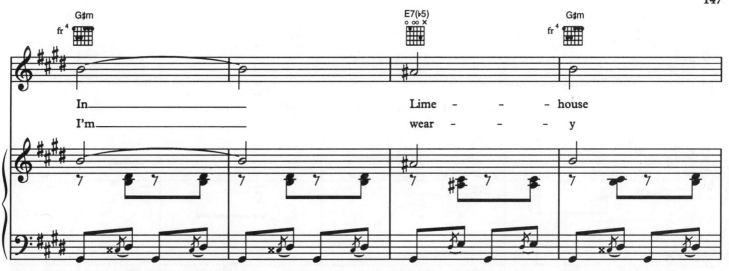

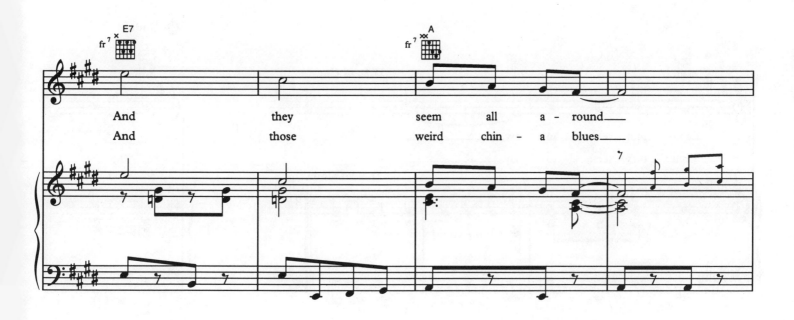

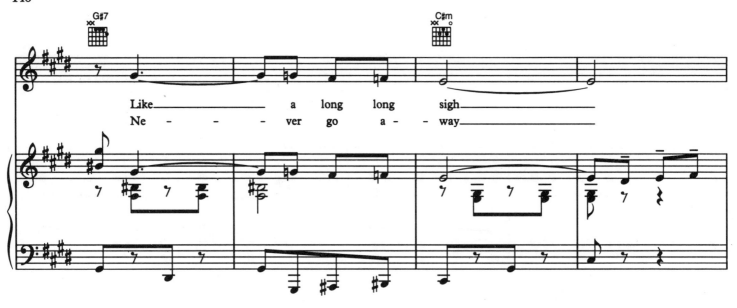

Like_____ a long long sigh_____
Ne — — — ver go a — — way_____

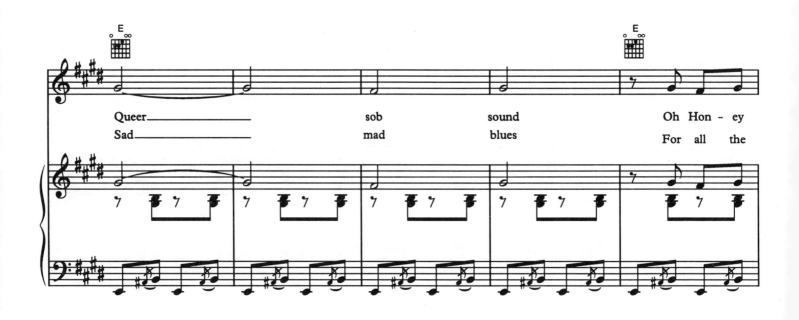

Queer_____ sob sound Oh Hon - ey
Sad_____ mad blues For all the

Lamb they seem to cry._____
while they seem to say._____

LOVE ME OR LEAVE ME

Words by GUS KAHN
Music by WALTER DONALDSON

Slowly (with feeling)

Love me or leave me, and let me be lone- ly You won't be -lieve me, and

I love you on- ly; I'd rath- er be lone- ly, than hap- py with some- bod- y else.

You might find the night -time, the right time for kiss -ing; But night -time is my time for

just rem - i - nis - cing, Re - gret - ting, in - stead of for - get - ting with some - bod - y else.

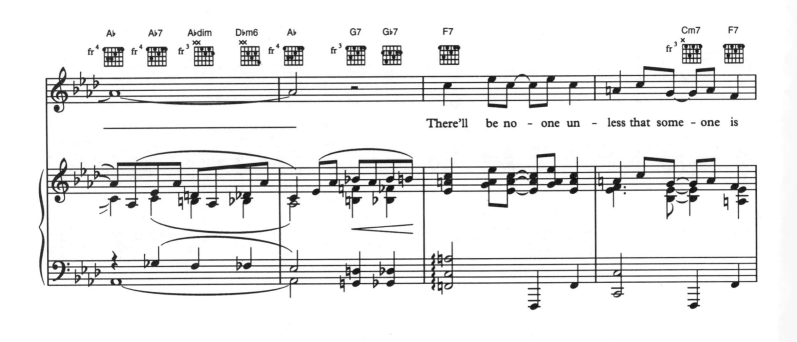

There'll be no - one un - less that some - one is

you;_____ I in - tend__ to be in - de - pen - dent - ly

blue._____ I want your love, but I don't want to bor - row, To

have it to-day, and to give back to-mor - row; For my love is your love, there's no love for no-bod- y else!

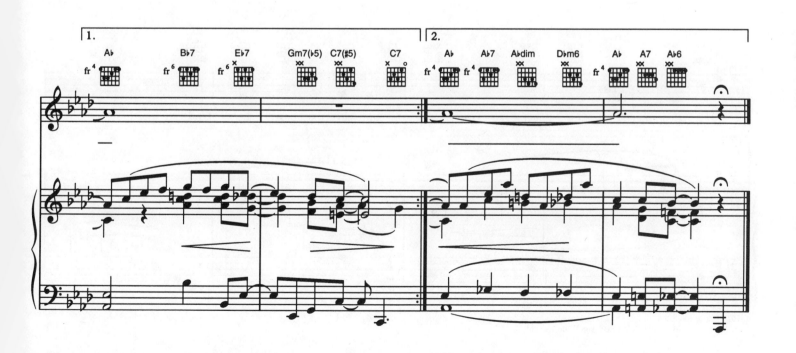

LOVER COME BACK TO ME

Words by OSCAR HAMMERSTEIN II
Music by SIGMUND ROMBERG

You went a-way, I let you, we broke the ties that bind;

I want-ed to for - get you and leave the past be - hind.

153

MA (HE'S MAKING EYES AT ME)

Words by SIDNEY CLARE
Music by CON CONRAD

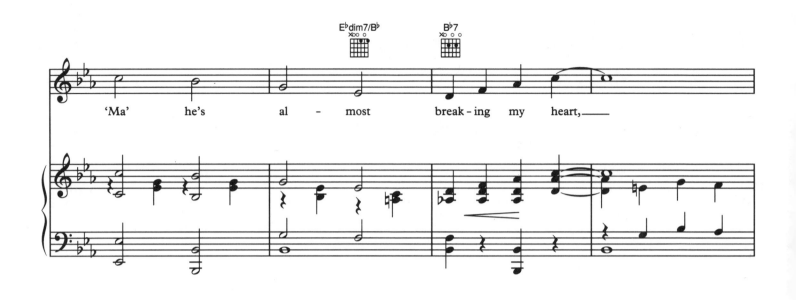

'Ma' he's al - most break - ing my heart,____

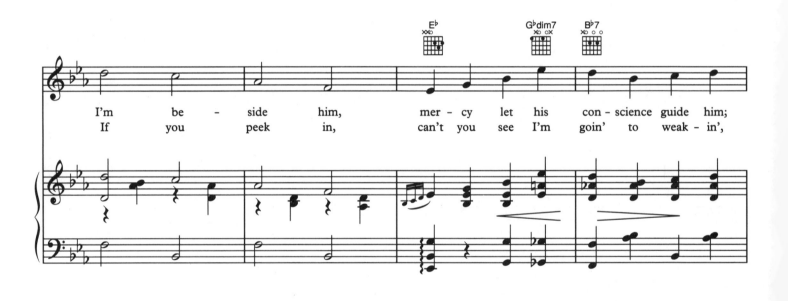

I'm be - side him, mer - cy let his con - science guide him;
If you peek in, can't you see I'm goin' to weak - in',

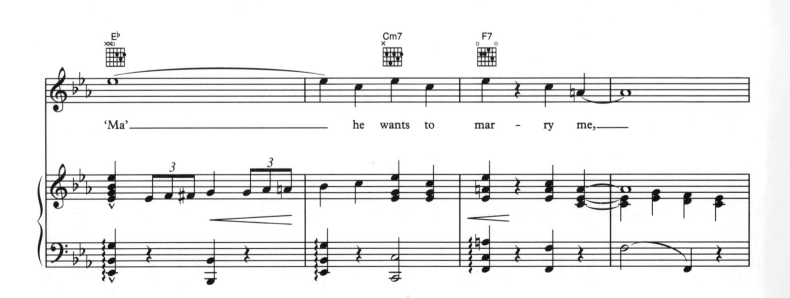

'Ma'_____ he wants to mar - ry me,____

159

be my hon - ey bee,   ev - 'ry min - ute
                                                             Ma I'm meet - ing

he gets bold - er,   now he's lean - ing   on my should - er,   'Ma'_____ he's kiss - ing
with re - sis - tance, I shall hol - ler for as - sis - tance,

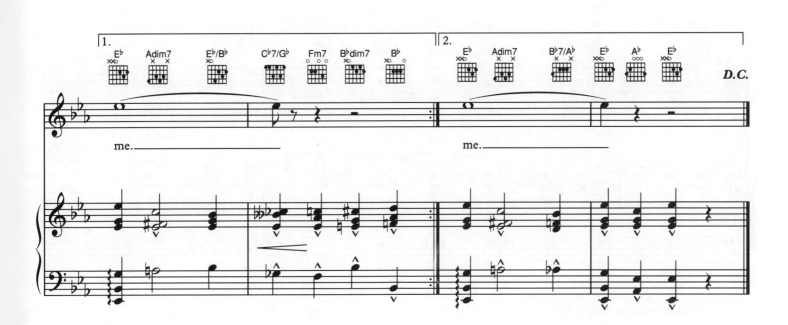

me._____   me._____   D.C.

MAKIN' WHOOPEE!

Words by GUS KAHN
Music by WALTER DONALDSON

MANHATTAN

Words by LORENZ HART
Music by RICHARD RODGERS

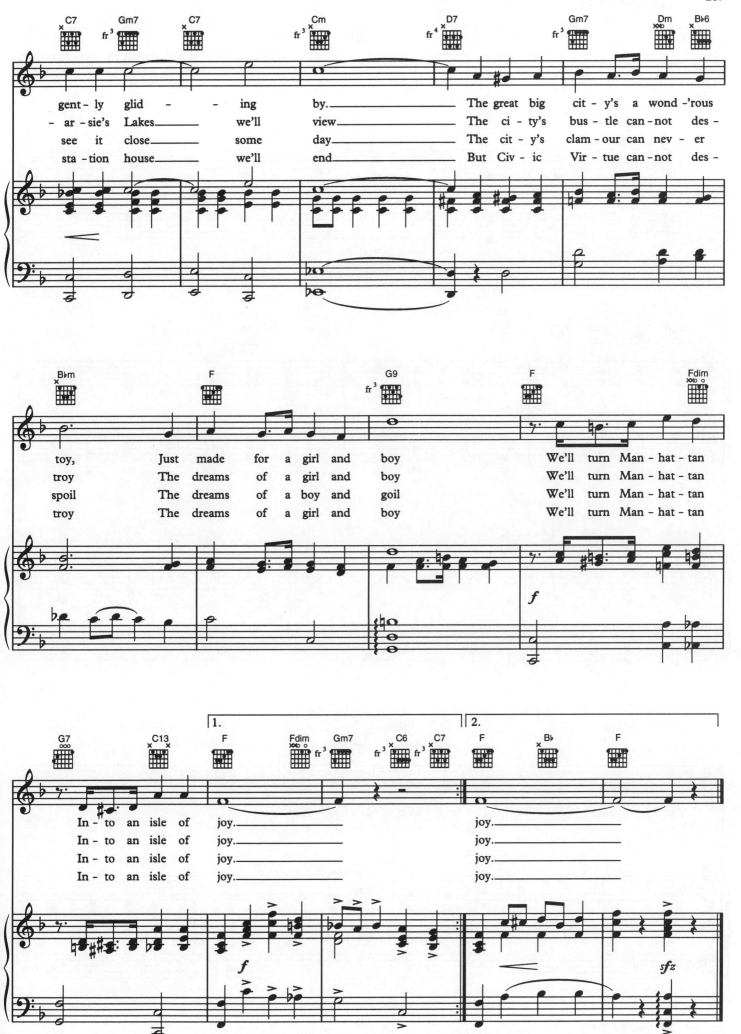

MARGIE

Words and Music by BENNY DAVIS, CON CONRAD
and J RUSSEL ROBINSON

You can talk a-bout your love af-fairs,_____
You can pic-ture me most ev-'ry night,_____

Francis Day & Hunter Ltd, London WC2H 0EA and Redwood Music Ltd, London NW1 8BD

ME AND MY SHADOW

Words by BILLY ROSE
Music by AL JOLSON and DAVE DREYER

Shades of night are fall - ing and I'm lone - ly,____
When the sun sets on the far ho - ri - zon____

stand - ing on the cor - ner feel - ing blue.____
and the par - lour lamps be - gin to glow,____

MEXICALI ROSE

Words by HELEN STONE
Music by JACK B TENNEY

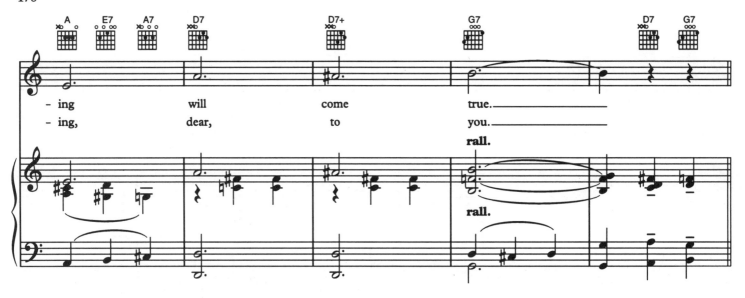

- ing   will   come   true.————————

- ing,   dear,   to   you.————————

rall.

rall.

Mex - i - cal - i Rose stop cry - - - ing, I'll come back to you some sun - ny

a tempo

a tempo

p - mf

day.———— Ev - 'ry night you'll know that I'll be pin - - ing, Ev - 'ry hour a

year while I'm a - way._____ Dry those big brown eyes and smile, dear,

Ban - ish all those tears and please don't sigh,_____ Kiss me once a - gain and hold

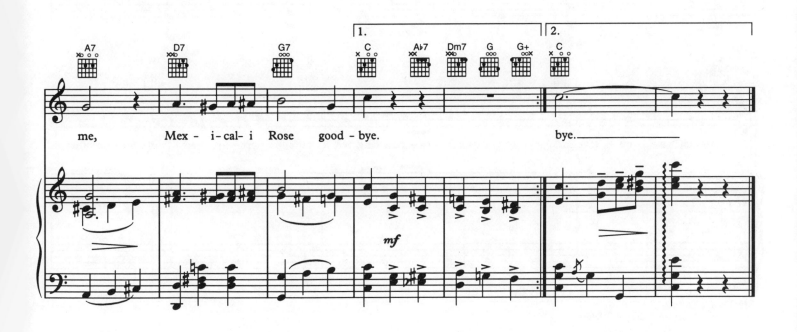

me, Mex - i - cal- i Rose good - bye. bye._____

MISS ANNABELLE LEE

Words and Music by SIDNEY CLARE, LEW POLLACK
and HARRY RICHMAN

MY BLUE HEAVEN

Words by GEORGE WHITING
Music by WALTER DONALDSON

Day is end-ing, Birds are wend-ing
Moon-beams creep-ing, Flow'rs are sleep-ing

Back to the shel-ter of Each lit-tle nest they love.
Un-der a star-lit way, Wait-ing an-oth-er day.

my blue heav- en._____ A turn to the right,_____

__ a lit - tle white light_____ Will lead you to my blue

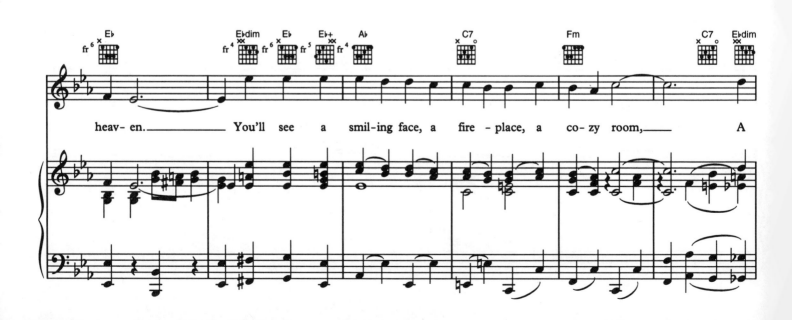

heav- en._____ You'll see a smil- ing face, a fire - place, a co- zy room,___ A

MY HEART STOOD STILL

Words by LORENZ HART
Music by RICHARD RODGERS

I laughed at sweet - hearts_____ I met at schools;_____
Through all my school - days_____ I ha - ted boys._____

___ all in - dis - creet hearts seemed ro - man - tic fools.
___ Those Ap - ril fool days brought me love - less joys.

MY MAMMY

Words by JOE YOUNG and SAM LEWIS
Music by WALTER DONALDSON

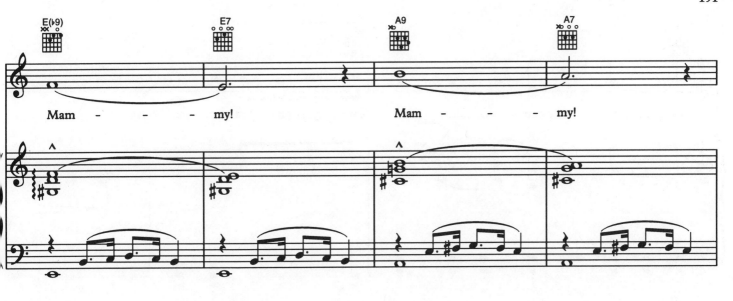

Mam - - my! Mam - - my!

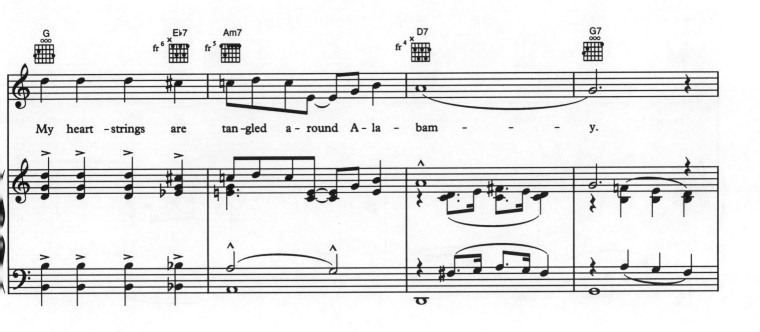

My heart - strings are tan - gled a - round A - la - bam - - y.

I'se_____ a - com - in!,_____ Sor - ry that I made you wait;

I'se ____ a - com - in!, ____ Hope and pray I'm not too late.

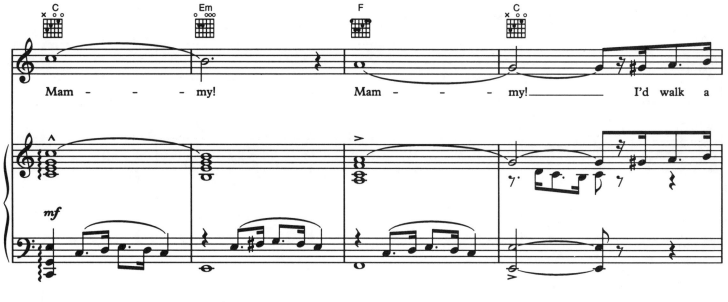

Mam - - my! Mam - - my! ____ I'd walk a

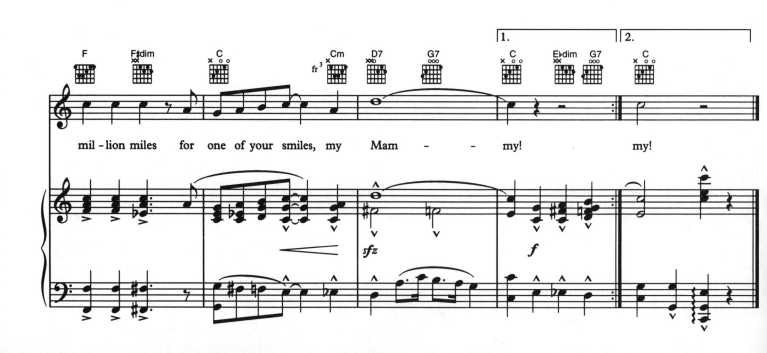

mil - lion miles for one of your smiles, my Mam - - my! my!

MY MOTHER'S EYES

Words by GILBERT L WOLFE
Music by ABEL BAER

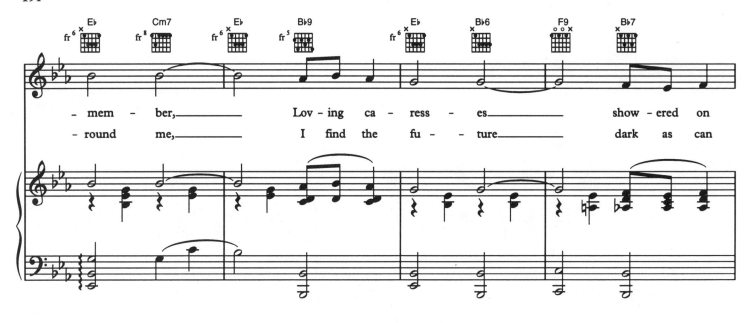

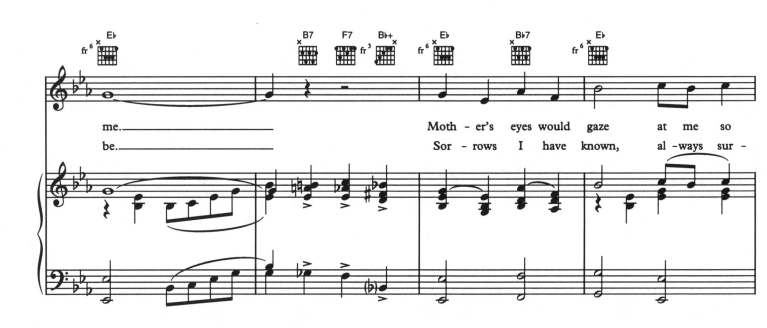

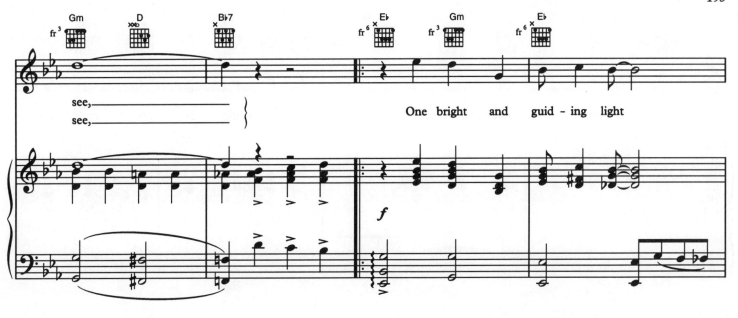

see,_____

see,_____

One bright and guid - ing light

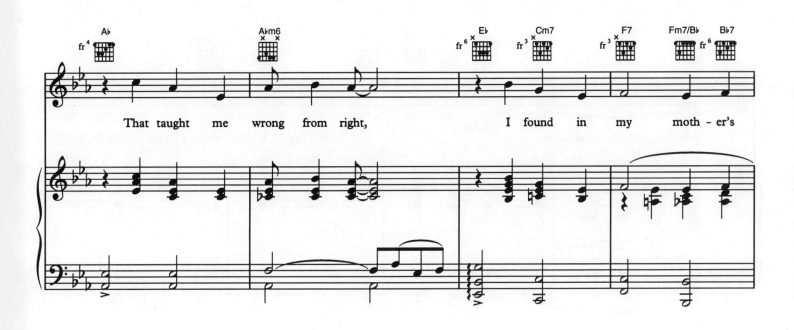

That taught me wrong from right,

I found in my moth - er's

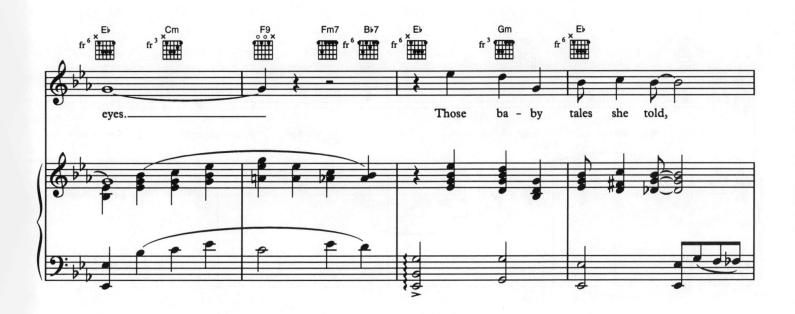

eyes._____

Those ba - by tales she told,

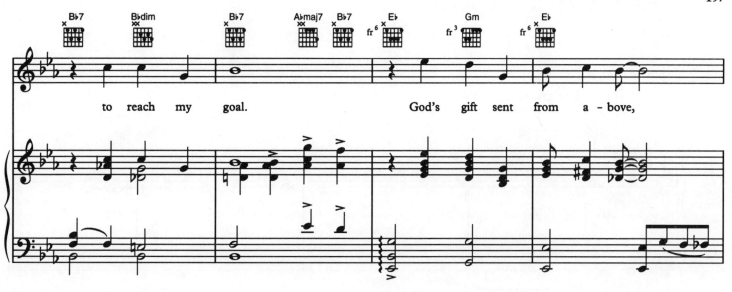

to reach my goal.   God's gift sent from a - bove,

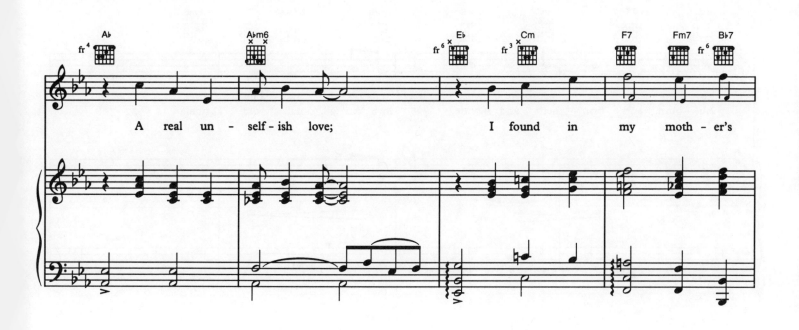

A real un - self - ish love;   I found in my moth - er's

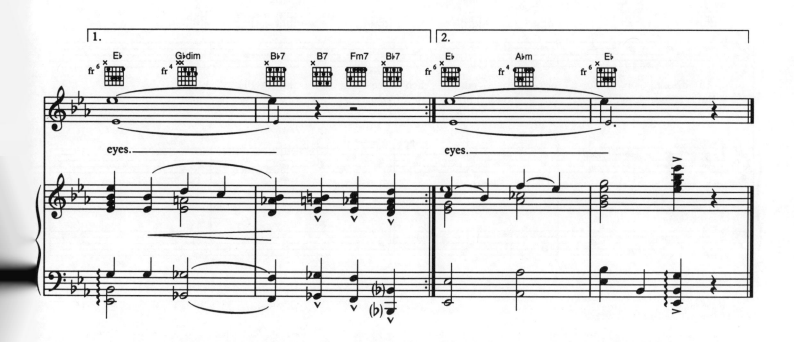

eyes._____   eyes._____

OH, LADY BE GOOD!

Music and Lyrics by GEORGE GERSHWIN and IRA GERSHWIN

Lively and graceful

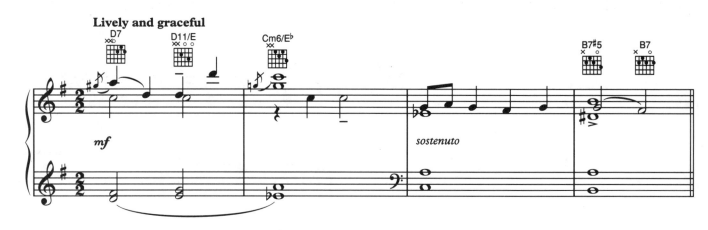

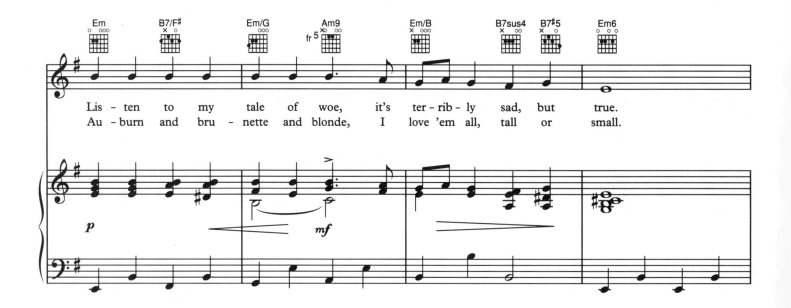

Lis-ten to my tale of woe, it's ter-rib-ly sad, but true.
Au-burn and bru-nette and blonde, I love 'em all, tall or small.

All dressed up, no place to go, each eve-ning I'm aw-f'ly blue.
But some-how they don't grow fond, they stag-ger but ne-ver fall.

PAINTING THE CLOUDS WITH SUNSHINE

Words by AL DUBIN
Music by JOE BURKE

This life's a play from the start, It's hard to play thro' a part
Each cloud you have on your mind, You'll find can be sil - ver lined

When there's an ache in your heart all day;____
If you'll just make up your mind to smile;____

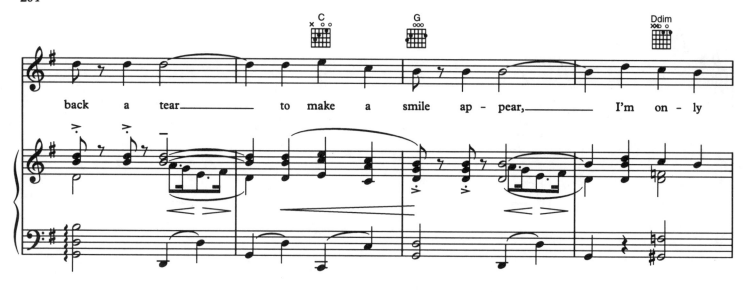

back a tear_____ to make a smile ap- pear,_____ I'm on - ly

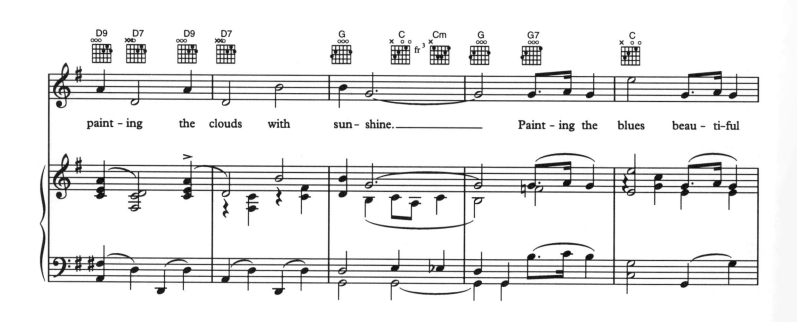

paint - ing the clouds with sun - shine._____ Paint - ing the blues beau - ti - ful

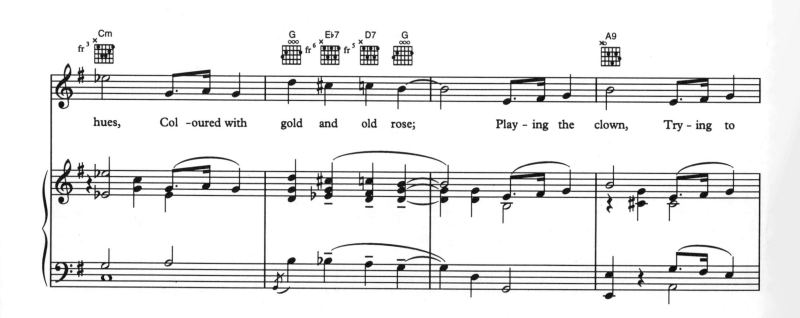

hues, Col -oured with gold and old rose; Play - ing the clown, Try - ing to

drown all of my woes; _____ Tho' things may not look bright _____

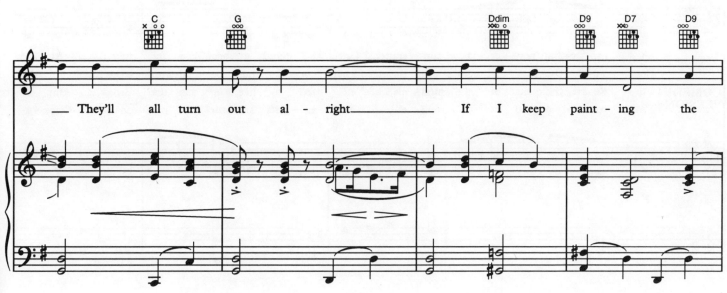

_____ They'll all turn out al - right _____ If I keep paint - ing the

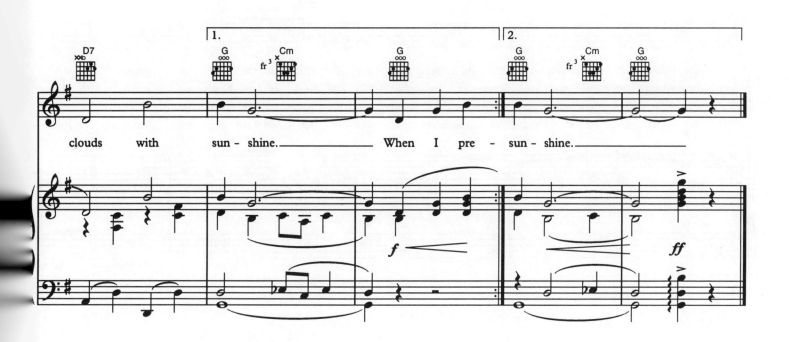

clouds with sun - shine. _____ When I pre - sun - shine. _____

ROSE OF WASHINGTON SQUARE

Words by BALLARD MacDONALD
Music by JAMES F HANLEY

A gar-den that nev - er knew sun - shine, Once shel -tered a beau - ti - ful rose,___ In the
But af - ter the sum - mer comes au - tumn, When flow - ers their pe - tals must close,___ For the

COMEDY VERSION
I'm Ro - sie, the queen of the mod - els,___ I used to live up in the Bronx, But I
I'm ter - ri - ble good as a mod - el, The ar - tists are stuck on my charms, Once a

sha - dows it grew, with - out sun - light or dew, As a child of the ci - ty grows.___ A
song - birds are still and the breez - es are chill, To the cheek of the blush - ing rose.___ The
wan - der'd from there down to Wash - ing - ton Square, And Bo - he - mi - an Hon - ky Tonks.___ One
fel - ler said he would paint Ve - nus from me, On - ly Ve - nus ain't got no arms.___ Rube

209

A ROOM WITH A VIEW

Words and Music by NOËL COWARD

SECOND HAND ROSE

Words by GRANT CLARK
Music by JAMES F HANLEY

dol - - lar / on 'em Sec - ond hand pearls___ I'm wear - ing sec - ond hand curls___

Sec - ond hand rings___ I'm sick of sec - ond hand things

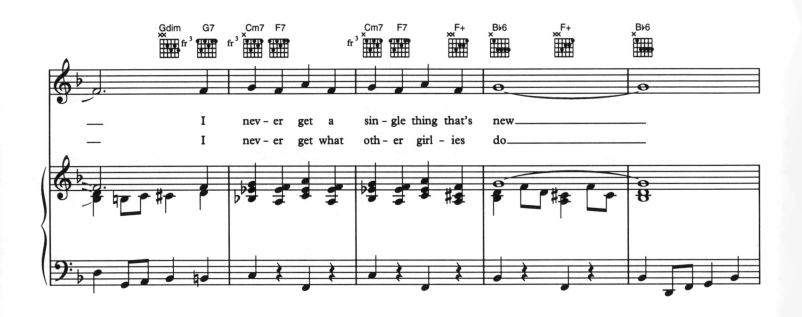

I nev - er get a sin - gle thing that's new___

I nev - er get what oth - er girl - ies do___

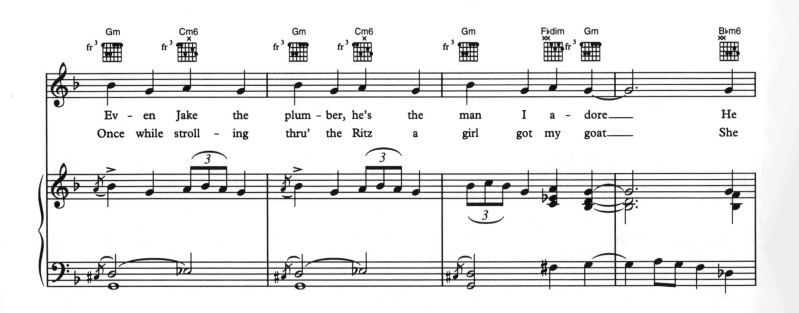

Ev - en Jake the plum - ber, he's the man I a - dore___ He

Once while stroll - ing thru' the Ritz a girl got my goat___ She

'S WONDERFUL

Music and Lyrics by GEORGE GERSHWIN and IRA GERSHWIN

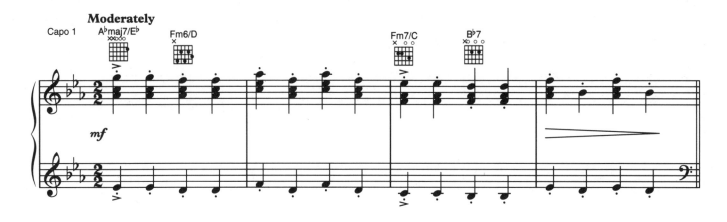

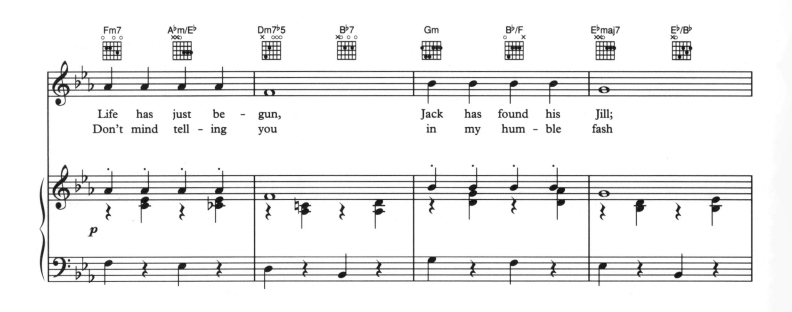

Life has just be - gun, Jack has found his Jill;
Don't mind tell - ing you in my hum - ble fash

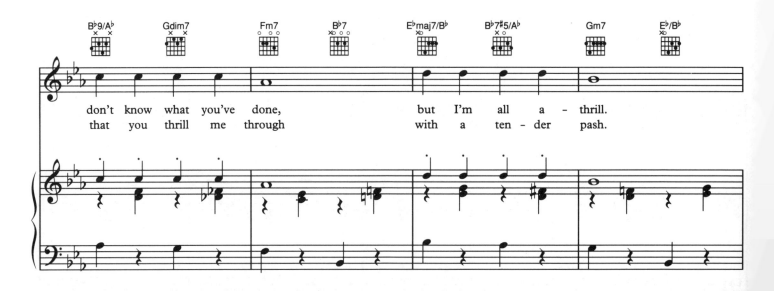

don't know what you've done, but I'm all a - thrill.
that you thrill me through with a ten - der pash.

SHE'S FUNNY THAT WAY

Words by RICHARD A WHITING
Music by NEIL MORET

223

SIDE BY SIDE

Words and Music by HARRY WOODS

227

sure it al - ways will. That's how I feel a - bout some - one, How some - bod - y feels a - bout

things we know we've got. We all for - get a - bout moon - light, As soon as we've giv - en our

me, We're sure we love each oth - er That's the way we'll al - ways be;_____

vow, But we'd all be so hap - py If we'd start and sing right now:_____

Oh! we ain't got a bar - rel of mon - ey, May - be we're rag - ged and fun - ny, But we'll

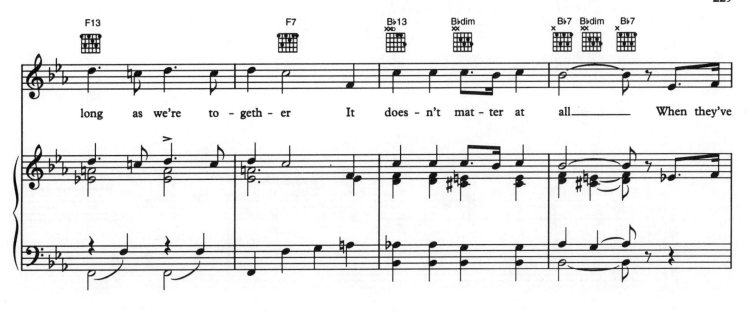

long as we're to - geth - er   It   does - n't mat - ter at   all_____   When they've

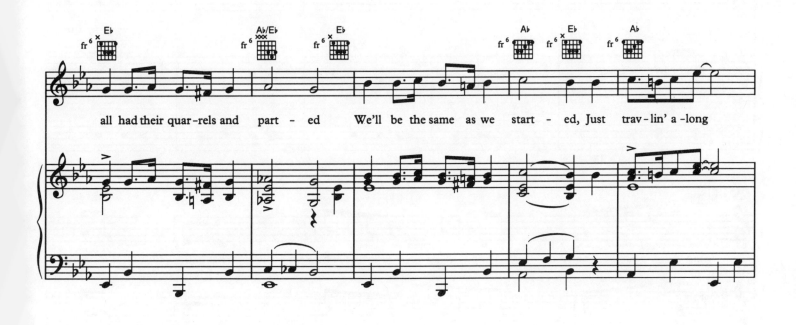

all had their quar-rels and   part - ed   We'll be the same as we   start - ed, Just   trav-lin' a -long

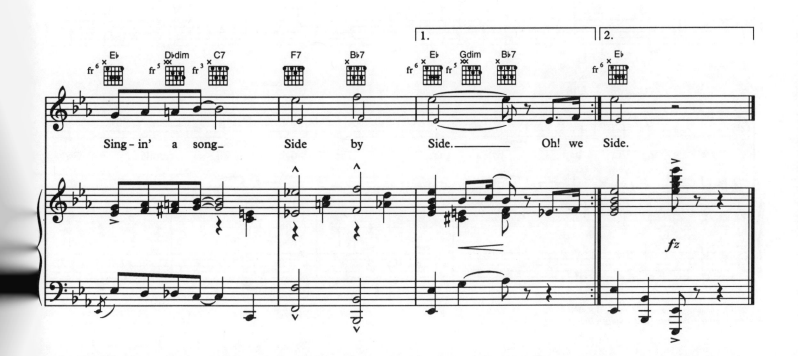

Sing-in' a song___   Side   by   Side._____   Oh! we   Side.

SINGIN' IN THE RAIN

Words by ARTHUR FREED
Music by NACIO HERB BROWN

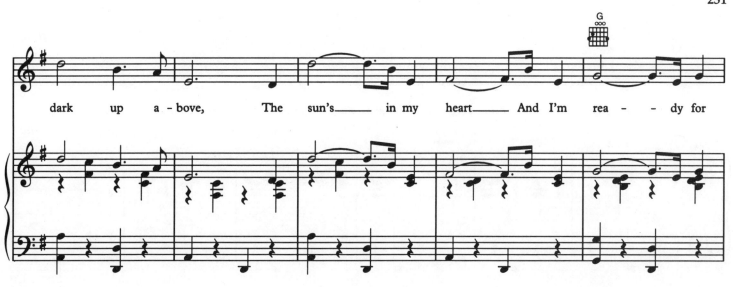

dark up a-bove, The sun's___ in my heart___ And I'm rea - - dy for

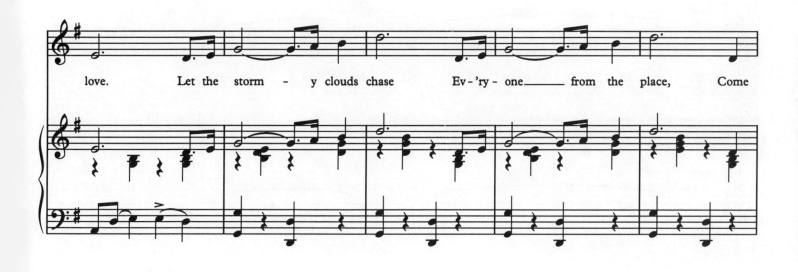

love. Let the storm - y clouds chase Ev-'ry-one___ from the place, Come

on___ with the rain, I've a smile___ on my face. I'll walk down the lane With a

hap - py re - frain, And sing - in'___ just Sing in' In___ The Rain._____

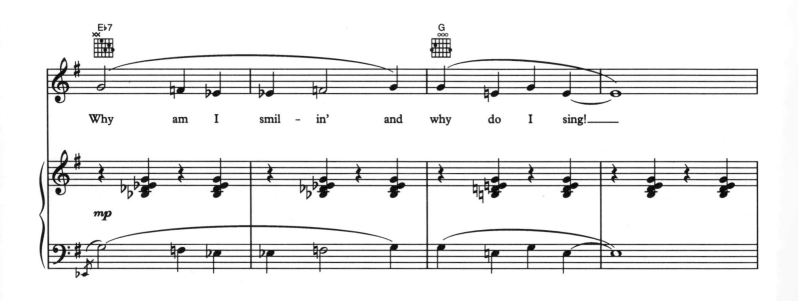

Why am I smil - in' and why do I sing!___

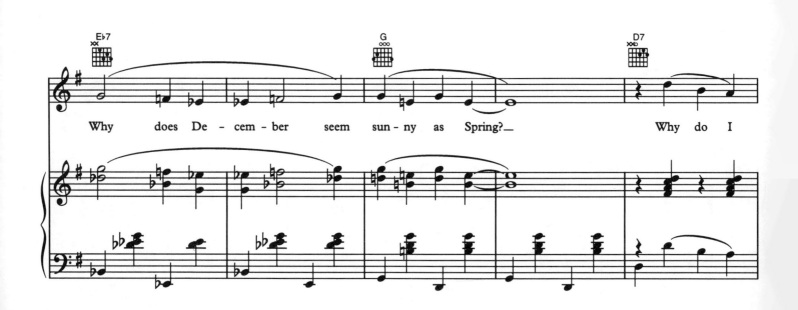

Why does De - cem - ber seem sun - ny as Spring?___ Why do I

get up each morn - ing to start___ Hap - py and het up with

joy in my heart?___ Why is each new task a tri - fle to do?___

___ Be - cause I am liv - ing a life full of you___ I'm

D.S. al Fine

SOMEBODY LOVES ME

Music and Lyrics by GEORGE GERSHWIN, BALLARD MACDONALD
and BUDDY De SYLVA

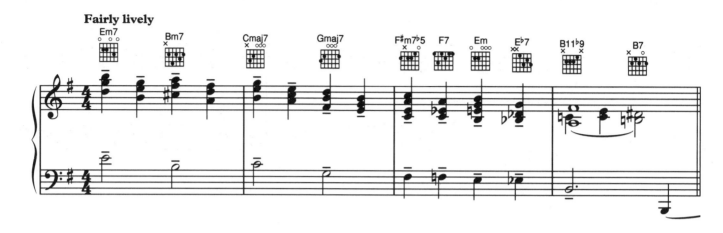

When this world be-gan, it was hea-ven's plan
Though I wait in vain, time and time a-gain,

there should be a girl for ev-ery sin-gle man.
no - one ev - er meets me down in Lov - ers' Lane.

SOMEONE TO WATCH OVER ME

Music and Lyrics by GEORGE GERSHWIN and IRA GERSHWIN

SPREAD A LITTLE HAPPINESS

Words by CLIFFORD GREY and GREATREX NEWMAN
Music by VIVIAN ELLIS CBE

days are long Keep on smil - ing through; And spread a lit - tle hap - pi - ness Till dreams come

true._____ Sure - ly you'll be wise___ to make___ the best___ of ev - -'ry

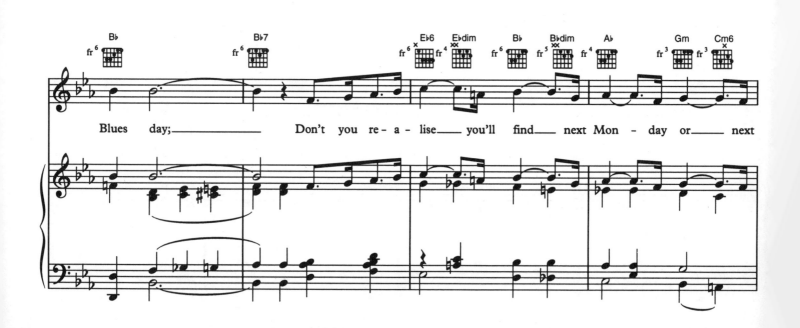

Blues day;_____ Don't you re - a - lise___ you'll find___ next Mon - day or___ next

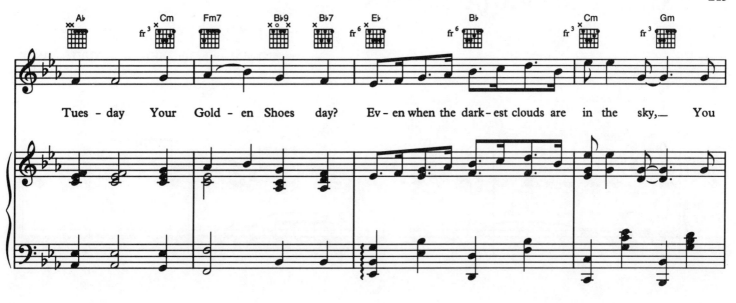

Tues - day Your Gold - en Shoes day? Ev - en when the dark - est clouds are in the sky,— You

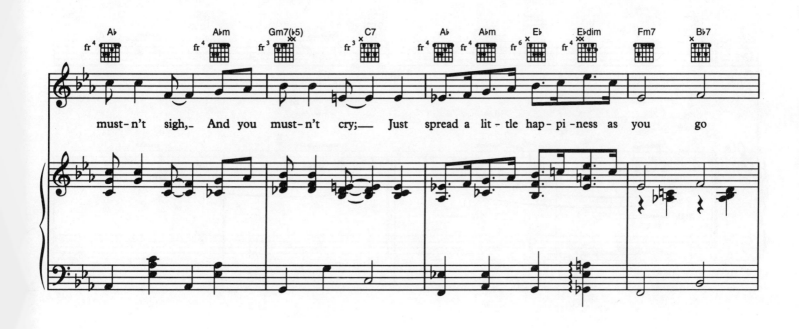

must - n't sigh,— And you must - n't cry;— Just spread a lit - tle hap - pi - ness as you go

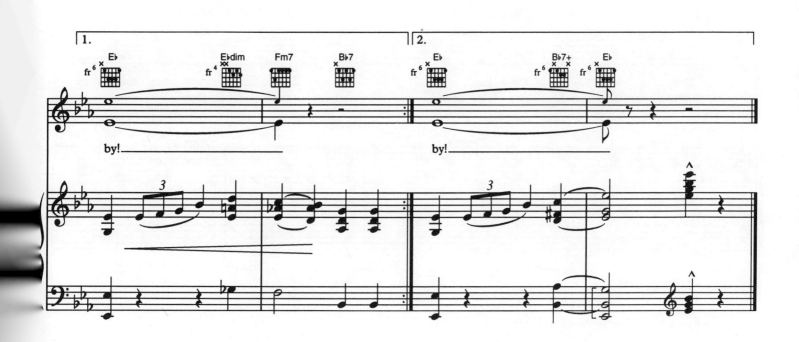

1.
by!_____

2.
by!_____

SWEET GEORGIA BROWN

Words and Music by BEN BERNIE, KENNETH CASEY
and MACEO PINKARD

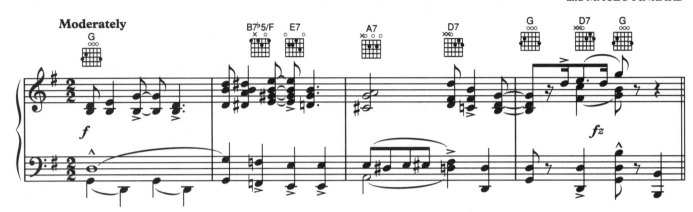

She just got here yes-ter-day.—
Brown-skin gals, you'll get the blues.

Things are hot here now, they say.— There's ___ a big change in
Brown-skin pals, you'll sure-ly lose— and ___ there's but one ex-

Francis Day & Hunter Ltd, London WC2H 0EA and Redwood Music Ltd, London NW1 8BD

TEA FOR TWO

Words by IRVING CAESAR
Music by VINCENT YOUMANS

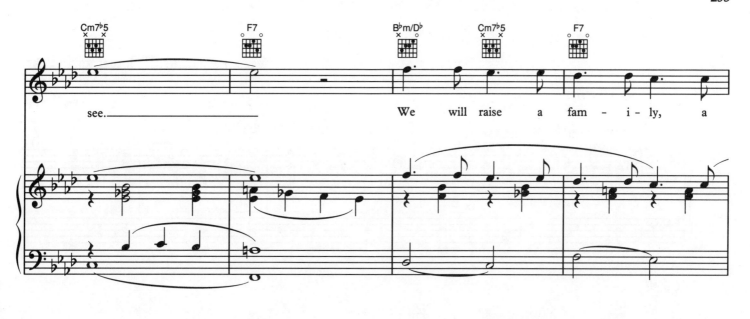

see._____ We will raise a fam - i - ly, a

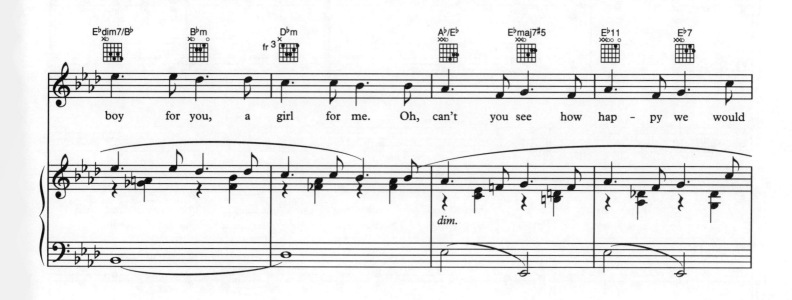

boy for you, a girl for me. Oh, can't you see how hap - py we would

be. be._____

D.C.

THERE'S A RAINBOW 'ROUND MY SHOULDER

Words and Music by AL JOLSON, BILLY ROSE
and DAVE DREYER

I'm hap-py, so hap-py, walk-ing on air.___ The why___ and the
I'm sing-ing, I'm sing-ing all the day long.___ The rea-son is

where-fore___ is some-one I care for.
sim-ple:___ two eyes___ and a dim-ple.

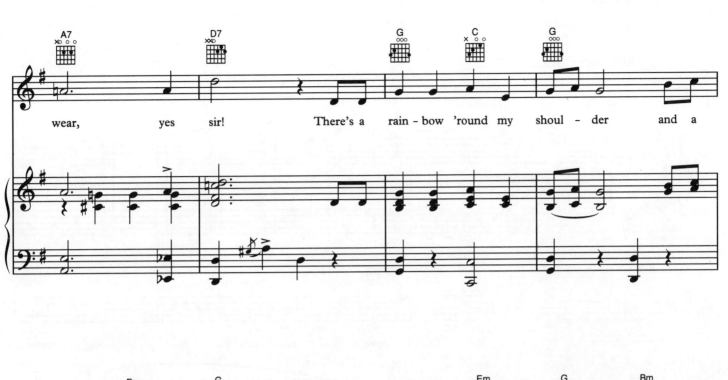

wear, yes sir! There's a rain-bow 'round my shoul-der and a

sky of blue a-bove,_____ and I'm shout-ing so the world will know that

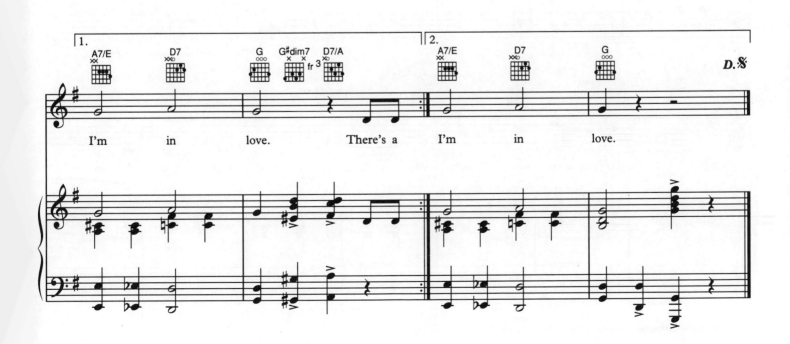

I'm in love. There's a I'm in love.

THREE O'CLOCK IN THE MORNING

Words by DOROTHY TERRISS
Music by JULIAN ROBLEDO

Slow waltz tempo

Lyrics:
It's three o'-clock in the morn - ing, we've danced all the whole night through_____ and day - light soon will be dawn - ing, just one more waltz with you._____ That mel - o - dy so en -

TIP TOE THROUGH THE TULIPS WITH ME

Words by AL DUBIN
Music by JOE BURKE

Shades of night are creep-ing, wil-low trees are weep-ing,
Come on out and pet me. Come and 'Ju-li-et' me.

old folks and ba-bies are sleep-ing._____
Tease me and sly-ly 'co-quette' me._____

THE SHEIK OF ARABY

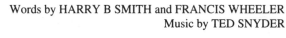

Words by HARRY B SMITH and FRANCIS WHEELER
Music by TED SNYDER

VALENCIA

Words by LUCIEN BOYER and JACQUES CHARLES
English words by ERIC VALENTINE
Music by JOSE PADILLA

Va - len - cia!_____ Land of o - range groves and sweet con - tent, You called me from a - far____

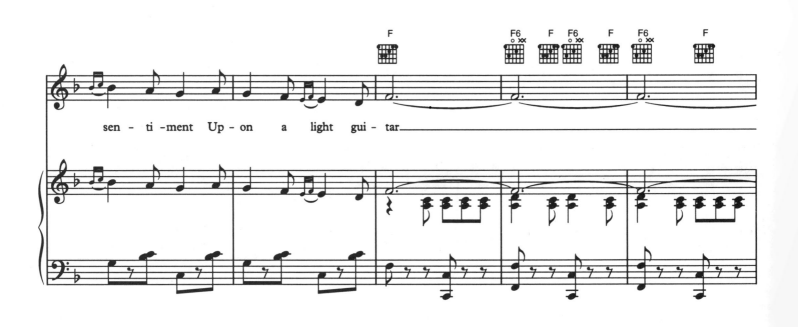

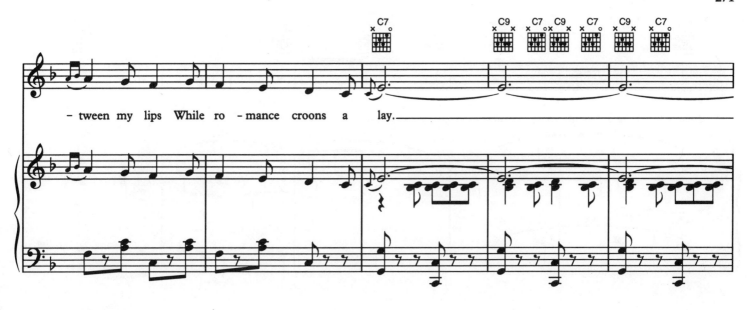

-tween my lips While ro -mance croons a lay.

— Va - len - cia!_____ Where a trou - ba -dour, be-

-neath the moon, Once stole my heart a - way._____ In my

dreams I hear you sing - ing Like you used to do. In the dusk each

sweet note bring - ing Mem - 'ry's of you____ Oh Car- lo, my Car- lo, where are____ you?____ Your

love I am need - ing,____ Be - lov - ed I wait in the moon - light, Just to hear you

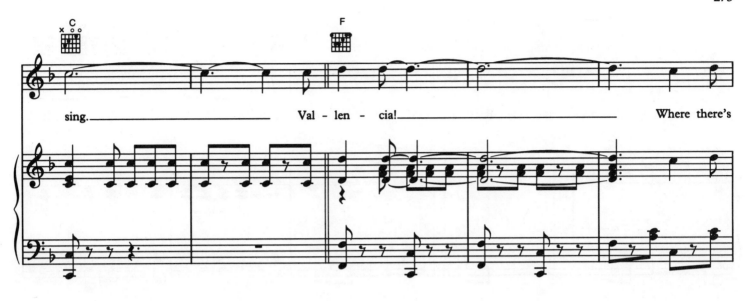

sing._____ Val - len - cia!_____ Where there's

pas - sion in the songs a lov - er sings be -neath the moon._____

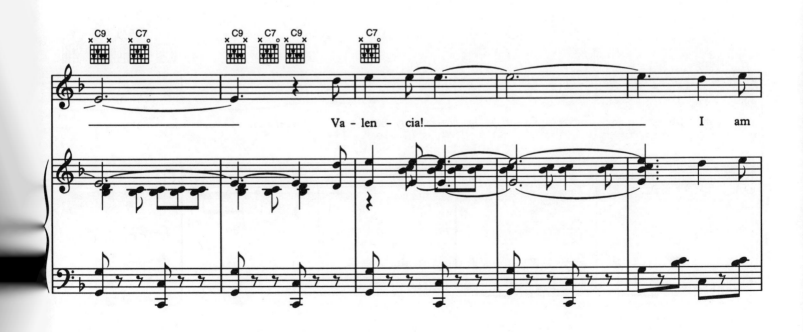

Va - len - cia!_____ I am

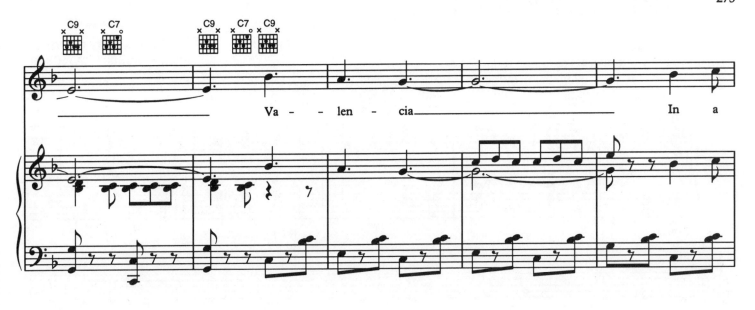

Va - - len - cia _____ In a

scent - ed o - range grove I'm yearn - ing For the love of you. _____

rall. un poco e morendo

rall. un poco e morendo

a tempo

a tempo

WHEN DAY IS DONE

Words by BUDDY De SYLVA
Music by ROBERT KATSCHER

WHEN MY SUGAR WALKS DOWN THE STREET

Words and Music by GENE AUSTIN,
JIMMY McHUGH and IRVING MILLS

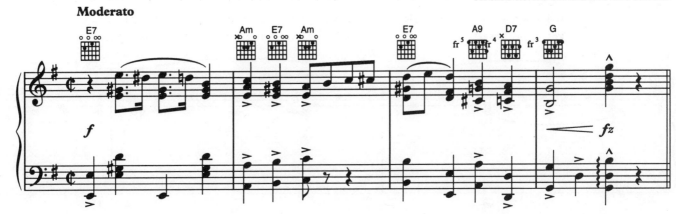

I know a thing or two   And I'm tell-ing you
I like my cof-fee sweet,   Ev-'ry-thing I eat

I've got a won-der-ful gal.   She's got the cu-test smile,
Must have some su-gar on top.   I'm tell-ing you the truth,

WHEN THE RED, RED ROBIN COMES BOB, BOB BOBBIN' ALONG

Words and Music by HARRY WOODS

WHEN YOU AND I WERE SEVENTEEN

Words by GUS KAHN
Music by CHARLES ROSOFF

Valse Moderato

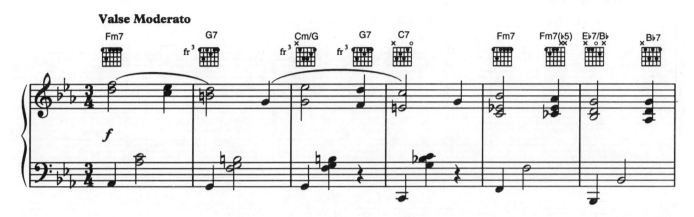

Once more I hold you to my heart_____ As
You loved me in the old-en days,_____ _____ When

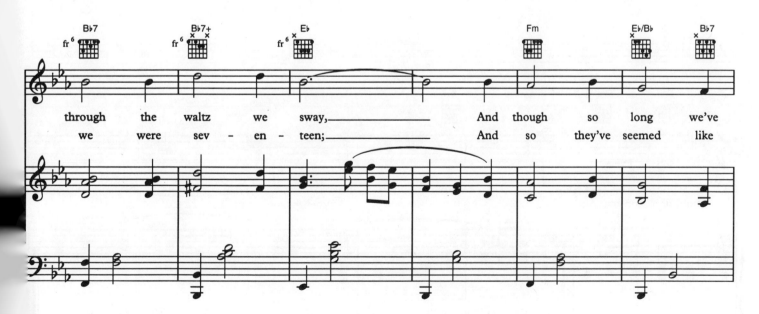

through the waltz we sway,_____ And though so long we've
we were sev - en - teen;_____ And so they've seemed like

©24 Bourne Co, USA
:cis Day & Hunter Ltd, London WC2H 0EA

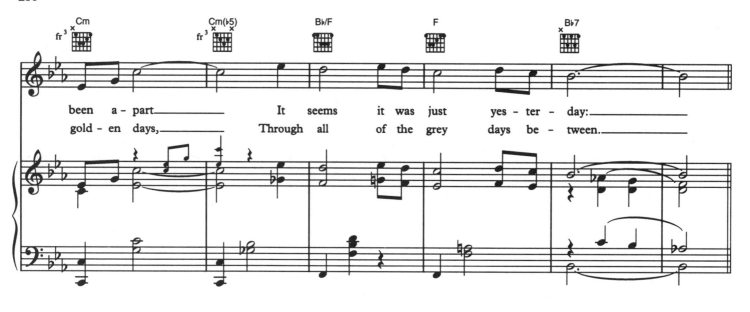

been a – part_____ It seems it was just yes – ter – day:_____
gold – en days,_____ Through all of the grey days be – tween._____

When you and I were sev – en – teen And life and love were

new;_____ The world was just a field of green, 'Neath

287

WHO

Words by OTTO HARBACH and OSCAR HAMMERSTEIN II
Music by JEROME KERN

Who_____ would I ans - wer yes

to?_____ Well, you ought____ to guess who._____
Darned if I_____ can guess who._____

No - one but you!____
No - one but you!____

WHY DO I LOVE YOU

Words by OSCAR HAMMERSTEIN II
Music by JEROME KERN

WHISPERING

Words and Music by JOHN SCHONBERGER,
RICHARD COBURN and VINCENT ROSE

Hon - ey, I have some - thing to tell
When the twi - light shad - ows are fall - -

you, And it's worth while list - en - ing to_____
- ing, And the wea - ry world is at rest_____

Put your lit - tle head on my should - - - er,
Then I'll whis - per just why I know, dear,

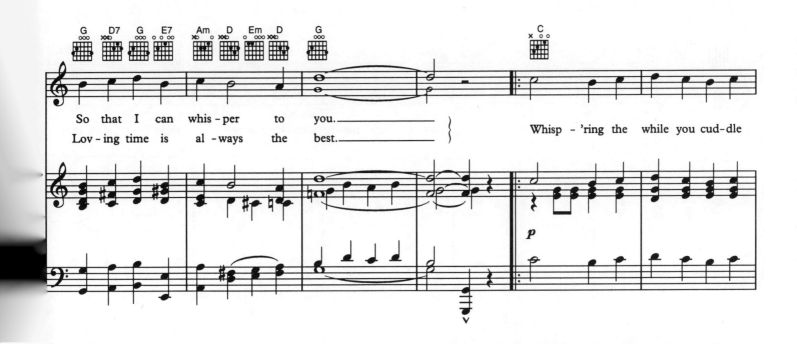

So that I can whis - per to you._____
Lov - ing time is al - ways the best._____

Whisp - 'ring the while you cud - dle

near _____ me, _____ Whisp - 'ring so no - one near can hear

me; _____ Each lit - tle whis - per seems to cheer _____ me;

I know it's true, There is no - one but you, You're whisp - 'ring just

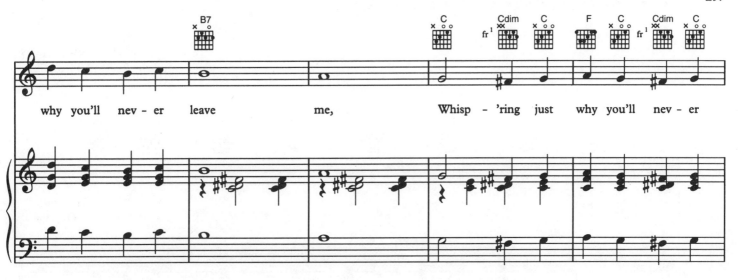

why you'll nev - er leave me, Whisp - 'ring just why you'll nev - er

grieve me: Whis - per and say that you be - lieve me,

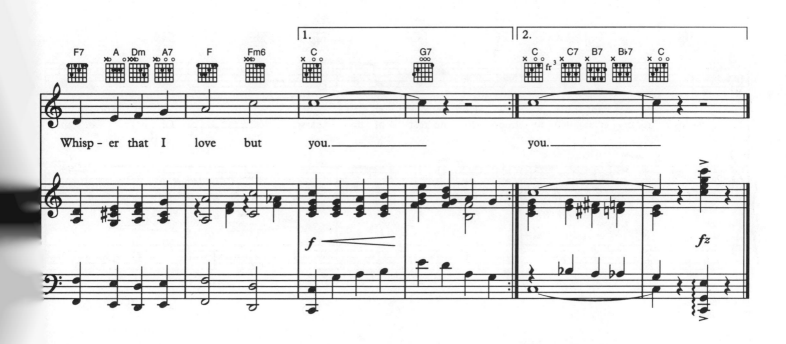

Whisp - er that I love but you._____ you._____

WITH A SONG IN MY HEART

Words by LORENZ HART
Music by RICHARD RODGERS

Though I
Oh, the

know that we meet ev - ery night and we could – n't have changed since the last time, to my
moon's not a moon for a night and these stars will not twin – kle and fade out, and the

joy and de - light, it's a new kind of love at first sight. Though it's
words in my ears will re - sound for the rest of my years. In the

por - tals to me. Can I help but re - joice

that a song such as ours came to be? But I al - ways knew

I would live life through with a song in my heart for

1. a tempo

2.

D.C.

you. you.

THE WORLD IS WAITING FOR THE SUNRISE

Words by EUGENE LOCKHART
Music by ERNEST SEITZ

Sweet - ly you_ are dream - ing, As the dawn comes slow - ly stream - ing;

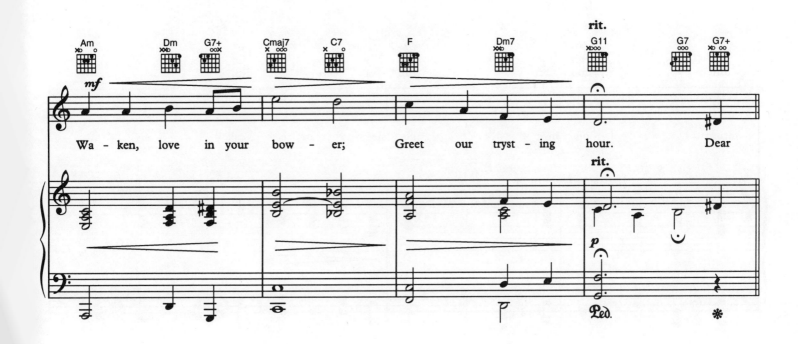

Wa - ken, love in your bow - er; Greet our tryst - ing hour. Dear

Slower, but with a certain swing, espressivo

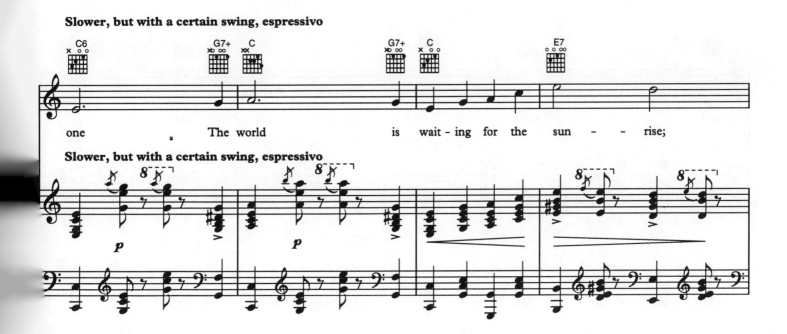

one . The world is wait - ing for the sun - - rise;

Slower, but with a certain swing, espressivo

Tempo I

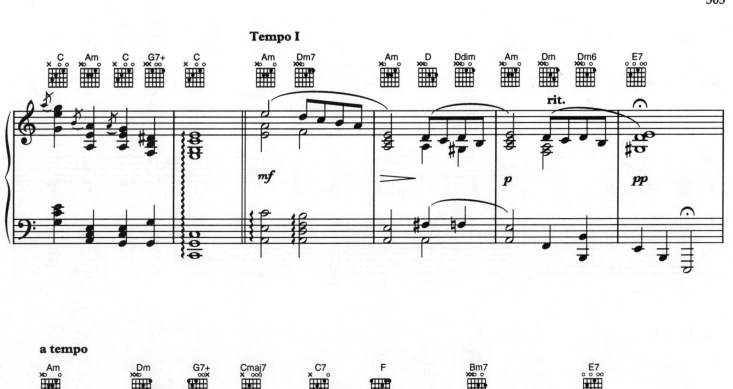

a tempo

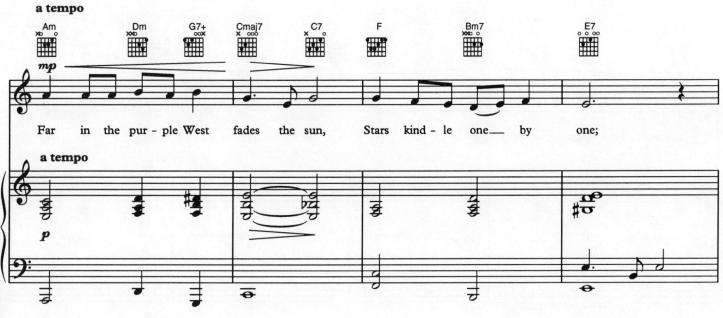

Far in the pur – ple West fades the sun, Stars kind - le one__ by one;

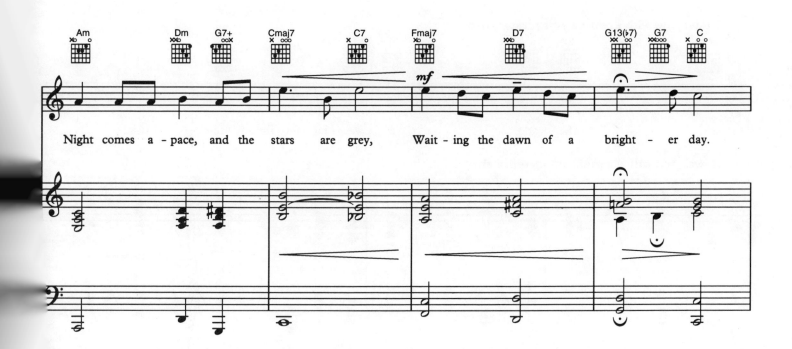

Night comes a - pace, and the stars are grey, Wait - ing the dawn of a bright - er day.

WONDERFUL ONE

Words by DOROTHY TERRISS
Music by MARSHALL NEILAN, PAUL WHITEMAN
and FERDE GROFE

My Won - der - ful One, When - ev - er I'm dream - ing, Love's love - light a -

gleam - ing, I see.____ My Won - der - ful One, How my arms ache to

hold dear, To cud - dle and fold near to me.____ Just you, on - ly

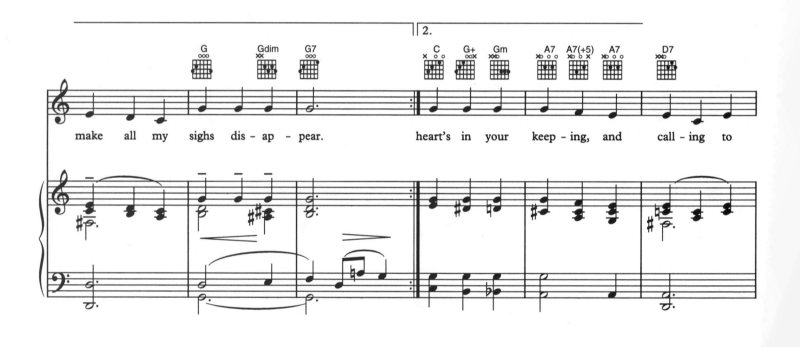

YES SIR, THAT'S MY BABY

Words by GUS KAHN
Music by WALTER DONALDSON

YOU'RE THE CREAM IN MY COFFEE

Words and Music by BUDDY De SYLVA, LEW BROWN
and RAY HENDERSON

100 YEARS OF POPULAR MUSIC

IMP
International
MUSIC
Publications

IMP's Exciting New Series!

100 YEARS OF POPULAR MUSIC

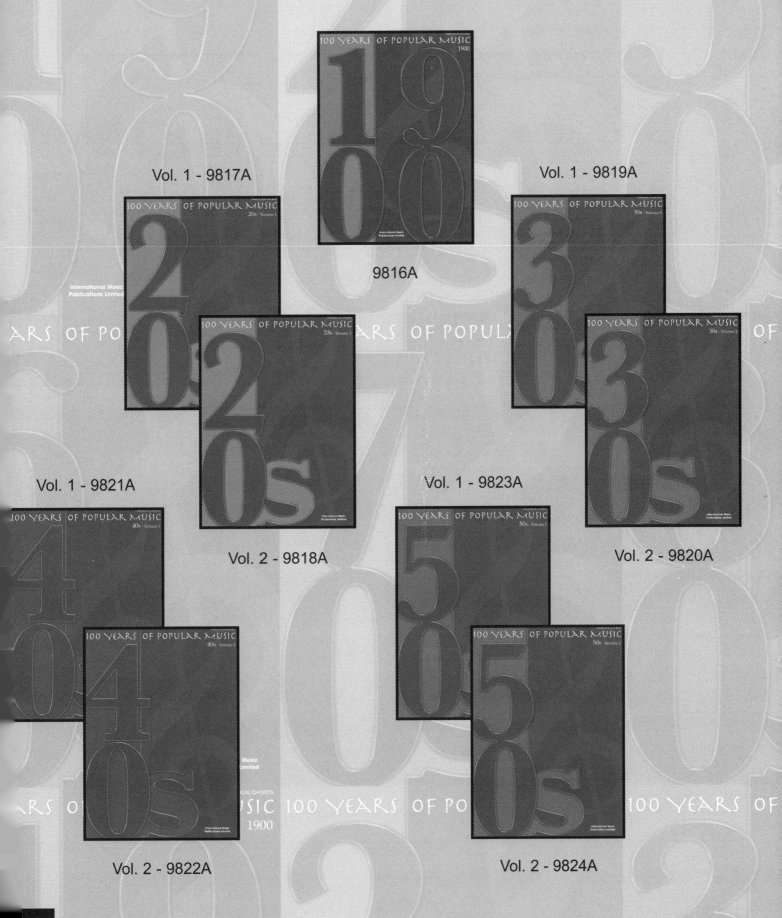

Vol. 1 - 9817A

9816A

Vol. 1 - 9819A

Vol. 1 - 9821A

Vol. 1 - 9823A

Vol. 2 - 9818A

Vol. 2 - 9820A

Vol. 2 - 9822A

Vol. 2 - 9824A

IMP's Exciting New Series!

100 YEARS OF POPULAR MUSIC

Vol. 1 - 9825A

Vol. 1 - 9827A

Vol. 1 - 9829A

Vol. 1 - 9831A

Vol. 2 - 9826A

Vol. 2 - 9828A

Vol. 2 - 9830A

Vol. 2 - 9832A

Vol. 2 - 9833A

IMP
International
MUSIC
Publications

IMP's Exciting New Series!